QC
122
D7

A. G. Drachmann

THE MECHANICAL TECHNOLOGY OF GREEK AND ROMAN ANTIQUITY

—

A STUDY OF
THE LITERARY
SOURCES

1963
Copenhagen – Munksgaard
Madison – The University of Wisconsin Press
London – Hafner Publishing Co.

Published by Munksgaard
International Booksellers and Publishers, Ltd.,
6 Nørregade, Copenhagen K, Denmark.

*

Published simultaneously
in North and South America
by the University of Wisconsin Press,
430 Sterling Court,
Madison 6, Wisconsin, USA.
and in the British Commonwealth
by Hafner Publishing Company Ltd.
Star Yard, Carey Street,
London W.C.2, England

*

Published simultaneously as vol 17 of Acta Historica
Scientiarum Naturalium et Medicinalium.
Edidit Bibliotheca Universitas Hauniensis.

*

Printed in Denmark by
AARHUUS STIFTSBOGTRYKKERIE

CONTENTS

PREFACE

The purpose of this book is to study the literary sources of the mechanical technology of Greek and Roman Antiquity. The chief work is Heron's Mechanics, which is found in Arabic only, but has been edited with translation into French in 1893 and German in 1900. I have translated into English all the parts dealing with mechanical technology, but not those that contain only geometry or statics. Some chapters that reproduce a lost work by Archimedes on the centre of gravity I propose to deal with somewhere else.

As a commentary to Heron I have added a few chapters from the Mechanical Problems ascribed to Aristoteles, some chapters from the 10th book of the Architecture of Vitruvius, and some chapters from the 49th book of Oreibasios.

In every case I have presented a translation into English and a commentary; where my interpretation differs from that of the editors, I have discussed the text; but such discussions, which needs must bristle with Latin, Greek and Arabic words, I have kept at a minimum, because they cannot interest more than a small part of those readers to whom the rest of the book may appeal. I have reproduced always with my translation the figure from the MS, where there was a figure. The editions of Heron as a rule do not give the MS figures, but only a redrawing to show how the implement must have looked. I have commented unfavorably on this way of editing, and my work with photocopies of some of the MSS has shown me how much there is to be learned from the figures themselves; it is my hope that the reader will appreciate this special feature of my book.

Two sources of mechanical technology, the poliorcetics and the belopoiics, I have treated more cursorily, since they have been edited with reproductions of the MS figures and with constructions of models of the catapults; the reader can safely be referred to these excellent works. I feel, indeed, that the treatment of Heron's Mechanics and Oreibasios is really not finished till I have made models of all the engines; but that has not been possible.

From the Carlsberg Foundation I have obtained a grant for preparing my book, and I wish to express my sincere gratitude for this very great help; also to the Statens Almindelige Videnskabsfond for a grant to procure necessary books of reference.

To many other institutions and persons I owe a debt of gratitude. For permission to reproduce the microfilms I thank the Bibliothèque Nationale, Paris, the Trustees of the British Museum, London, the University Library, Leiden, and the Bibliotheca Apostolica Vaticana, Rome. To dr. Per Krarup, Director of the Danish Academy at Rome, who examined a MS for me, and to Mr. D. E. Strong, assistant keeper of the British Museum, who examined the pumps in that collection, I also offer my best thanks.

Finally I wish to record my gratitude to my colleagues of the Royal Library, the University Library, both departments, and the Danmarks Tekniske Bibliotek, all of Copenhagen, for their never failing helpfulness.

Svends Allé, Lyngby, Denmark

A. G. Drachmann

LIST OF ILLUSTRATIONS

Abbreviations: Heron's works: HD Dioptra HM Mechanics HP Pneumatics. MSS:
B British Museum H Copenhagen L Leiden My Mynas Codex, Paris.
MP Aristoteles: Mechanical Problems
O Oreibasios
P Pappos. MSS: P Paris   V Vatican
V Vitruvius

The Literary Sources of Ancient Mechanics
and their Dates

The literary sources of our knowledge of ancient mechanics are first of all the technical writings still extant; next the casual references found in historical, philosophical or poetical works.

For many years the problems of the dates of the technical writings have been discussed; but to me it seems that in most cases it is now possible to reach a reasonably reliable conclusion. Nevertheless some writers on the history of ancient technology seem to regard the dating of a technical author as something to be done by intuitive reasoning or wishful thinking with a complete disregard of the available material. Two instances may illustrate this queer phenomenon.

Writing on "Machines" in A History of Technology (68), B. Gille (42) refers us to a note on p. 708 for the dates of Ktesibios, Philon, and Heron. This note, written by A. R. Hall in a chapter on Military Technology (43), runs: "The dates of the Greek mechanicians—Ctesibius, Philo of Byzantium, and Hero of Alexandria—are all very uncertain. Therefore the 'inventions' described here cannot be exactly dated either. In order not to attribute to them an excessive antiquity, we may cautiously assume that Ctesibius lived about the beginning of the first century B.C., that Philo flourished about A.D. 1, and that Hero was a younger man who died (say) about A.D. 75. Older historians accepted dates about a century earlier than these, but we shall not be far out if we regard the peak of inventiveness with regard to war-machines as coinciding with the most vigorous age of the Roman Empire."

On p. 636, B. Gille himself gives the date of Philon of Byzantium as c. 200 B.C.

Fr. Lammert, writing s.v. Poliorketiker in the Pauly Realencyclopädie, reviews the dates for Heron and finds it most probable, with Hoppe, that he lived about 133 B.C. as a contemporary of Hipparchos. He quotes O. Neugebauer and A. Rome for the date 62 A.D., and mentions L. Reinhardt (time of Augustus) and R. Meier. But he disregards the fact that Rome and Neugebauer date Heron by an eclipse of the moon, which according to astronomical calculations took place in the year 62 A.D. To set aside this date it would be necessary to prove either that Heron did not write the Dioptra, where the eclipse is mentioned, or that his eclipse is not the one of the year 62, or that the eclipse in question did not take place in that year. Lammert merely finds it "most probable" that Heron lived about 133 B.C.

I shall now make a chronological list of the existing technical works and of the men to whom certain inventions have been attributed.

ARISTOTELES: Mechanical Problems (2). Aristoteles lived from 384–322 B.C. This work is generally assumed not to be from his own hand, but to belong to the peripatetic school; it may be from the time of Straton, who was head of the school from 287–268 B.C.

KTESIBIOS. According to Vitruvius (131), Ktesibios was the son of a barber; when trying to mount an adjustable mirror in the shop, he found that the counterweight sliding down a narrow canal compressed the air, which escaped with a loud noise. This led to the invention of the cylinder and plunger, and so to the force pump and the water-organ, and a catapult worked by compressed air. He also invented another catapult and a scaling ladder; further the water-clock and a number of mechanical and pneumatic devises, such as singing birds to call the hours, and other toys. Since Vitruvius takes his information from a book written by Ktesibios himself (132), we may accept it as authentic.

Athenaios in the Deipnosophists gives us two different dates for Ktesibios. He quotes (3) an epigram by the poet Hedylos about a singing cornucopia made by Ktesibios for the statue of Arsinoe, the deified spouse of Ptolemaios Philadelphos; this statue was set up about 274 B.C., and Hedylos lived about this time; so this date is fairly certain. In another connexion (4) Athenaios quotes one Aristokles for the fact that Ktesibios was a barber and invented the water-organ, and that he lived under Ptolemaios Physkon (145–116 B.C.). From this Susemihl (126) concluded that there were two inventors of that name; others believe that the text in Athenaios is at fault. I have gone over the evidence in the Centaurus (24) and conclude that there was one person only, living about 300–270 B.C. Anybody is at liberty to belive in one Ktesibios about 270 B.C. and another about 145–116 B.C., but other dates are not admissible without proof.

ARCHIMEDES, the greatest mathematical and mechanical genius of Antiquity, died in 212 B.C., 75 years old. All of his still extant works are theoretical only; we know that he wrote only a single book about practical mechanics, on how to build a spherical planetarium. He is credited with the invention of the water-snail, the endless screw, the compound pulley, and cranes and other engines of hitherto unknown power for the defense of Syracuse. In two small papers (26, 28), I have tried to show that the modern tendency to deny him some of these inventions is without foundation.

BITON (5). Under this name we have six chapters dedicated to King Attalos; four containing catapults, one a scaling-ladder, and one a siege-tower. It is a compilation: the six machines are ascribed to five different men.

Two of these men, Charon and Poseidonios, are otherwise unknown, though the author states that Poseidonios made his siege-tower for Alexander the Great, that is about 330 B.C. Zopyros the Tarantine is identified by Diels (12) as a Pythagorean, whose name is found in Iamblicos, and who lived not later than 350 B.C. Damis the Colophonian, who made the scaling-ladder, may be Damios the Colophonian, nauarchos of Eumenes II, about 168 B.C. Isidoros the Abydene was nauarchos under Antiochus III, in 191 B.C.

If Damis is Damios, it is unlikely that the king to whom the book is dedicated is Attalos I (241–197 B.C.); it might be either Attalos II (159–138 B.C.) or Attalos III (138–133 B.C.). An absolute *terminus ante quem* is found in the fact that the title is quoted by Athenaios in his Deipnosophists 14:634A, from about 300 A.D.; but it is remarkable that the name is not found in Vitruvius.

The most curious thing about this work is that no one so far has been able to understand it. This does not mean that here and there in the book difficult or unintelligible passages are found; the fact is that no one has presented us with an acceptable description, founded on and in accordance with the text and the illustrations, of even one single one of these six machines.

U. von Wilamowitz-Moellendorff (138) declares that it is beyond him; Schramm has given a vivid description of the difficulty he found in interpreting the text, and he presents his reconstructions with the greatest diffidence—as well he may, since they cannot be made to fit the text or the figures. The scaling-ladder with its large screw is certainly an armchair invention, for the container for the counterpoise will take 44 tons of lead where 4 tons were plenty. Part of the text is incredible and does not fit the figure.

Anyway, as long as we cannot understand Biton's text, he is no use for us in the study of ancient technology.

VITRUVIUS wrote his book on Architecture (129) about 25 B.C. and dedicated it to Augustus. It is divided into 10 books, of which the last one contains much information on means of transport and other technical matters for the use of the builder. He writes an atrocious Latin, but he knows his business.

ATHENAIOS THE MECHANICIAN has written a book on poliorcetics, that is on how to capture fortified towns (107). It is dedicated to one Marcellus, but not the one who captured Syracuse in 212 B.C., but rather Augustus's son-in-law of that name, which would date it about 27 B.C.

HERON OF ALEXANDRIA (44). From the hand of this versatile author we have books on Pneumatics, on Automatic Theatres, on a Dioptra (a combined theodolite and water-level, with instructions for its use), on Catapults; also a text-book on Geometry, together with later elementary mathematical text-books wrongly attributed to him. All these are extant in the original Greek. He has written a text-book on Mechanics, which has come down to us in an Arabic translation only, except for some fragments preserved by Pappos; this is by far our best source of knowledge about ancient mechanical technology.

In a paper from 1938 O. Neugebauer (85) has called attention to the fact that the data he gives in his Dioptra for an eclipse of the moon will fit an eclipse that took place in the year 62 A.D. and none other. Since this date is determined by astronomical computation it is irrefutable, as long as the Dioptra is ascribed to Heron.

PAPPOS lived at the time of Diocletian (285-305 A.D.) and wrote a large Collection on mathematical topics; the 8. book (90) treats of mechanics and contains many fragments of earlier authors.

OREIBASIOS was physician-in-ordinary to the emperor Julian (361–363 A.D.). He has written a large book on medicine (88), which is of interest here because he describes some engines for resetting dislocated limbs. For this purpose the surgeons used mechanical constructions not otherwise employed.

The Mechanical Problems of Aristoteles

This book (2) is generally attributed not to Aristoteles himself, but to the peripatetic school, say 280 B.C. It is a theoretical work and it is only accidentally that it gives us information about mechanical tools actually in use. No figures are found in the MSS; but they are reconstructed from the text.

The title of the treatise ought to be "On the Lever", for with very few exceptions it explains all the mechanical questions discussed by reference to the principle of the lever.

The Lever itself is derived from the Circle, as it is set forth in the introduction, which is a queer compound of metaphysics and mechanics. Some things, we read, occur according to nature; other things are contrary to nature, but they are made to occur by our skill. As the poet Antiphon has it: "By skill we conquer, where we are baffled by nature." It is "against nature" that a smaller weight should lift a greater weight, as it is done by the lever.

Now the circle, or wheel, is a strange combination of natural and "unnatural" phenomena: the centre is at rest, while the circumference moves; the periphery is concave and convex at the same time; when the wheel turns, one part goes "forwards" and another "backwards" at the same time; the moving radius returns to the place from which it set out; and different points along the same radius move at different speeds.

If two wheels touch, one will turn one way, the other the other way; a third wheel will turn the same way as the first wheel. This place has been interpreted as if cogged wheels were meant, but that is quite unlikely. The text makes no mention of teeth on the wheels, and the whole ting is explained as "those wheels of bronze or iron which they dedicate in temples". Heron describes such a wheel, called ἀγνιστήριον (59). The *hagnistērion* is "a wheel of bronze, placed at the entrance to the temple; this is what those who enter the temples use to turn." The touch of the metal was supposed to have a purifying effect. This apparatus lends itself to mechanical miracles; if the mechanism was hidden behind the wall, several wheels would be seen to move this way or that when the *hagnistērion* was turned. But since only a very slight resistance had to be overcome, the thing could be worked by friction alone, and there is no need to assume cogged wheels in the absence of any positive evidence that they were used.

The balance, which turns about an axle or a string, is derived from the wheel, and the lever is derived from the balance.

So far the introduction. The rest of the work consists of a discussion of 35 problems.

It is not necessary here to go into all the problems raised and answered; if they deal with static mechanics, the answers are generally correct; but when movement comes in, the author is out of his depth, as in finding out why a very small rudder can turn a very large ship (Problem 5), or how to explain the movement of two wheels of unequal size, fixed on the same axle and rolling either along the smaller or along the larger circumference. This problem is also attacked by Heron, as will be seen on p. 32. I shall single out the chapters in which we learn about practical mechanics.

> Problem 11. "Why are burdens more easily carried by rollers than upon carts, although the carts have large wheels while the rollers are small? It is because on the rollers there is no friction at all, but on the carts there is the axle, where there is friction; for it (the burden) presses on it both from above and sideways. The burden upon the rollers is moved on two points, the ground supporting from below and the burden lying above; for the circle turns at both these points and is pushed forward the way it travels."
>
> Problem 13. "Why are the larger grummets more easily turned round the yoke (of the lyre) than the smaller ones, and of windlasses of the same size the thinner ones turned more easily by the same power than the thicker ones? It is because the windlass and the yoke are centres, and the distances from them are the radii. Those of the greater circles are turned more swiftly and further by the same power than those of the smaller circles, for by the same power the end furthest from the centre is moved more swiftly. This is why they put the grummets on the yoke as tools with which to turn more easily; in the thin windlasses that which is outside the wood becomes more, but the radius is the same."

The last sentence means that if the handspake of the windlass is of the same length, the power will be increased, if the thickness of the drum is made smaller, because the ratio between the radius of the drum and the length of the handspake is increased.

The yoke or upper cross piece of the lyre was round; each string was held by a thick ring of leather strips plaited round the yoke. To tune each string the player had to turn this grummet (75).

> Problem 17. "Why are great weights and large bodies pulled apart by the wedge, small as it is, and why does a great pressure arise? It is because the wedge

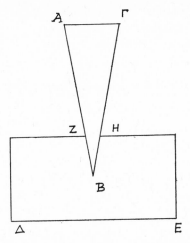

Fig. 1. Mechanical Problems no. 17. Text p. 14 sq.

consists of two levers opposite one another, and each of them has both the weight and the hypomochlion which both lift and press. Also the travel of the blow makes the weight, which hits and puts to movement, great; and because that which is moved moves by swiftness, it exerts an even greater force. Great powers belong to it, small as it is; therefore it is not seen to set in movement beyond the worth of its size. Let the wedge be ABΓ; the thing wedged ΔEHZ. Then AB becomes a lever, the weight is that which is below B, the hypomochlion ZΔ. Opposite this is the lever BΓ. AΓ, when struck, makes use of both of them as a lever; for the point B is lifted."

This attempt to explain the action of the wedge in terms of the lever is not very successful. See fig. 1.

Problem 18. "Why is it that if you place two pulleys on two pieces of wood that come together against one another and put a rope round the pulleys, with one end of the rope fastened to one of the pieces of wood, while the other end is pressed against or passed over the pulleys, and you then pull the end of the rope, you can lift a great weight, even if the pulling power is small? It is because the same weight is drawn by a smaller power, if it is levered, than by hand alone. The pulley works in the same way as the lever, so that one single pulley draws more easily, and draws a far heavier thing by one drawing than by hand; the two pulleys will lift swiftly more than double. For one pulley draws even less than if it drew by itself alone, when the rope is placed along the other pulley; for this makes the burden still less. And so if the rope is put through more pulleys, a great difference is made by few pulleys, so that if by the first one the burden draws four minas (17.46 kg), it will draw far less through the last one. And in house-building they move great weights; they pass the rope from one

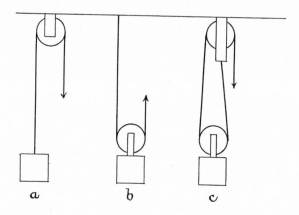

Fig. 2. Mechanical Problems no. 18. Text p. 15 sq..

pulley to another, and from that to windlasses and handspakes; that is the same as making many pulleys."

The theoretical explanation is not correct. A single pulley arranged as in fig. 2a will give no more power than a direct pull, but it will often give greater ease. A single pulley arranged as in fig. 2b will halve the power necessary (apart from friction), and the simple pulley, fig. 2c, will do no more.

Oreibasios ascribes the invention of the *trispaston* to Apellis or Archimedes, see p. 178; but while Vitruvius uses the word *trispastos* for a simple pulley, in Oreibasios the word means a geared winch; see p. 180.

As for the word *polyspaston*, Vitruvius uses it about an arrangement with three parallel ropes pulled by three gangs of workmen, see p. 147, while Pappos, quoting Heron, uses it about a compound pulley, see p. 55. In Oreibasios, who on the authority of Galenos ascribes its invention to Archimedes, we may take it to mean a geared winch with more than three axles; see p. 172.

Anyway, the author of the Mechanical Problems seems to have known both the simple and the compound pulley, which dates them before, say, 285 B.C.

Problem 21. "Why do the physicians find it easier to extract the teeth by adding the weight of the forceps than by the bare hand alone? Is it because the tooth slips more easily from the hand than from the forceps? But really the iron slips more easily than the hand and does not envelope the tooth, for the flesh of the fingers, being soft, clings more and adapts itself. No, it is because the for-

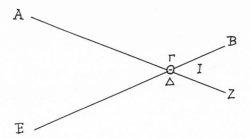

Fig. 3. Mechanical Problems no. 21. Text p. 16 sq.

ceps consists of two levers working against one another, with a common fulcrum where the tongs are put together; so they use the instrument to get easier extraction". (See fig. 3). "Let one end of the forceps be A, the other, the one that extracts, B; then one lever is AΔZ, the other BΓE, the fulcrum ΓΘΔ. The tooth is in the gap I; it represents the weight. The physician takes hold with B and Z together and moves at the same time. When he has moved it, he takes it out more easily with his hand than with the instrument."

The forceps was used, then, to loosen the tooth, not to draw it out. But in Heron's Mechanics the forceps seems to have been used for the whole operation. See p. 93.

Problem 22. "Why are the nuts easy to crack without a blow in the instruments that they make for cracking them? For the power of the movement and the violence, that is left out, is great. Also you will crack it sooner by pressing it with a hard and heavy tool than with a wooden and light tool. It is because in this way the nut is pressed from both sides by two levers, and the heavy things are easily split by the lever". (See fig. 4). "For the tool consists of two levers having the same fulcrum, that is the joint marked A. Just as they are pulled apart by those that move the ends ΔΓ, so EZ are easily pulled together by a slight power. The same power, then, that the weight produces by the blow, will be produced by EΓ and ZΔ, since they are greater, being levers; when they are lifting, the lift comes from both sides, and in pressing they crush that which is at K. For the same reason, the nearer K is to A, the sooner it will be crushed; for the further the lever is from the fulcrum, the more easily it will move, and the greater the weight, by the same power. Now A is the fulcrum, ΔAZ is a lever, and so is ΓAE. The nearer then K is to the angle at A, the nearer it comes to the joint at A; and that is the fulcrum. So it is evident that ZE, if they are pressed together by the same power, must lift more. So that since the lifting comes from opposite sides, they must press more, and that which is pressed more is cracked sooner."

It would seem that nut-crackers were made both of metal and of wood. The use of the word "lift" for the action of the crackers is queer;

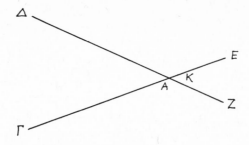

Fig. 4. Mechanical Problems no. 22. Text p. 17 sq.

but in the terminology of the lever that which is levered is always the "weight", and the action is to "lift" it, even if the action consists of bringing together the jaws of a forceps.

> Problem 28. "Why do they make well-sweeps the way they are? For they place the lead as an extra weight on the beam, while the bucket is the weight itself, whether it is empty or full. It is because the work is divided into two stages (for the bucket has to be dipped, and then drawn up), and it happens that it is easy to lower the empty bucket, but difficult to draw it up when full. So it pays to have it go down a little more slowly and then have the weight much lighter when it is to be drawn up. This is what the lead or the stone effects when it lies on the end of the sweep. For to him who lets it down the weight is greater than if he has to send down the empty bucket only; but when it is full, the lead, or whatever weight is found there, pulls it upwards. So the two movements are easier for him than the other way."

This is a very fair specimen of the author when he is best. The work contains very much of interest for the study of the history of theoretical mechanics; for the study of the practical application the chapters quoted here may suffice.

Heron's Mechanics

Introduction

Heron of Alexandria lived about A.D. 62, as stated on p. 12. In my dissertation from 1948 (23) I have tried to show that Heron, far from being "ein Banause", as Diels has it, or an ignoramus, as dr. I. Hammer-Jensen contends, was a man who knew his business thoroughly, who was acquainted with the whole field of mathematics, astronomy and mechanics of his time, and who was quite a skilful inventor. The adverse judgement is built upon the Pneumatics, a work which is very conspicuous among the books that have come down to us; but this is not a finished book, merely a compilation of notes, and it is only a part of a large production, which takes in the whole sphere of mechanics and a large amount of mathematics. The most outstanding trait of his authorship is its clarity. A man who is always able to present his subject in such a way that it is readily understood, is a man who understands it himself, and he is certainly not a fool or a bungler.

The Mechanics are found in an Arabic translation only, with just a few pieces preserved in Pappos to show that this is indeed a genuine work by Heron, not just something that has got his name attached to it.

The first edition (55) was made by Carra de Vaux, in 1893, from a single MS, found in the University Library at Leiden. He gives us a translation into French, an introduction, and some comments.

In 1900, the text was edited for B.G.Teubner by L.Nix, with a German translation (55). To the Arabic text W.Schmidt has added all the Greek fragments from Pappos, and excerpts from Vitruvius, Plinius and Cato, with a German translation, which add very much to the usefulness of the book.

Nix gives us an introduction, with discussion of the genuineness of the work, the MSS, the figures, the Greek words found in the Arabic text, and the language of the translator.

For the text, Nix uses four MSS. He has used personally the Leiden MS (L) and a written copy of a MS in Cairo (C); for a MS in the British Museum (B) he has had collations made by Carra de Vaux, and for a Constantinople MS (K) collations by the same and by Salih Zéhy Bey. There is a critical apparatus to show the variants; but when I have had occasion to consult my photocopies of the MSS, I have found that the apparatus is not always to be trusted.

But these few inaccuracies of the text seem a mere trifle compared with the way the figures are treated. When they are just mathematical diagrams, they are as a rule rendered correctly; but where they represent implements, the somewhat clumsy figures are redrawn to show what the thing looked like—according to the editor. The reader has no way of knowing how the figure in the MS looks, or whether indeed there is a figure or not. Carra de Vaux began this, and Nix prints his figures, unless he disagrees with him, when he makes his own interpretation.

Most of the figures have letters corresponding to letters in the text; this must mean that these figures are as old as the text, and that the reader has every right to see them in their original form, so that he can form his own opinion about them. In some cases no letters are found referring from the text to the figure, nor does the text mention any figure at all. Here the figure may be a later addition, especially if it is found in a single MS only; but even if all the MSS agree, it may have been made e.g. by Quṣṭâ ibn Lûqâ for his translation. On the other hand, it may have been made by Heron himself; and in any case it should be reproduced for the benefit of the reader. So I have used photocopies of two of the MSS for the figures (54).

For an edition of the Arabic text, a photographic reproduction of the figures would be the best way. But for a translation I do not think that it will do, for readers that are quite unacquainted with the Arabic alphabet would be unable to identify the printed letters with the handwritten letters, often unpunctuated, on the drawings. It would then be necessary either to change the letters in the photographic reproduction, which takes away part of its evidential value, or to make two figures, one with Arabic and one with Latin letters. (The way used by Carra de Vaux and Nix of putting Greek letters on the figures has little to recommend it; it comes no nearer to the original than a transliteration, and it makes it very troublesome for those who study the Arabic text to identify the letters in the figure). Now the figures are expressly made to be redrawn by any scribe who undertook to copy the text, and I think that I ought to be able to copy them just as well. As it turned out, I learned quite a lot from these attempts; and I think that the figures which I give, true copies drawn from the MS, with transliterated letters, or translations of the Arabic words, will be of more use to my readers than a photographic reproduction alone.

The transliterations are those of the Draft ISO Recommendation 353; only in the case of the letter ʿayin, transliterated ʿ, I have substituted the letter O. I hope that those readers who know Arabic will forgive me this tiny concession to their less fortunate fellows. Transliterations in the text of course follow the Recommendation.

In reading the Mechanics, we have to make allowances for the translation into Arabic, a language almost as far from Greek as it could be. The long Greek periods, with participles and subordinate clauses, have to be rendered by the paratactic arrangement of the Arabic, where so to say every other sentence has to begin with "and". In my translation I have followed the construction of the sentences closely, even though it results in a rather clumsy language; I feel as if the reader who does not know Arabic comes a little closer to the original in this way than if I had rewritten every passage to make a more idomatic English.

The superscription of the first book runs:

"In the name of God, the Merciful, the Compassionate, Lord aid by Thy "Mercy.

"The first part of the book by Heron on the lifting of heavy things. Abu "'l 'Abbâs Aḥmad ibn al-Mu'taṣim has ordered its translation from the Greek "language into the Arabic language, and Qusṭâ ibn Lûqâ from Ba'albak has "been charged with the translation."

The Khalif Abu 'l 'Abbâs reigned from 862 to 866, which gives us a date for the translation; Qusṭâ ibn Lûqâ, or Costa ben Luka, is well known as the translator of many Greek works. He shows himself here to be a man who understands his text thoroughly, and who is very careful not to make any errors. A characteristical example is found in Book 3, ch. 13. The Greek word for a press-beam is *oros*, which also means a mountain. So he translates: "the balk which is called mountain". I think that we can regard his translation as an intelligent and faithful rendering of the original.

The Mechanics are divided into three Books: an introduction, an exposition of the theory of the five powers: the windlass, the lever, the pulley, the wedge, and the screw; and some examples of their practical use. It is a textbook on theoretical and practical mechanics for architects and contractors. The whole work is well arranged, very different from the queer jumble of the Pneumatics; but there are several chapters that are conspicuously out of place.

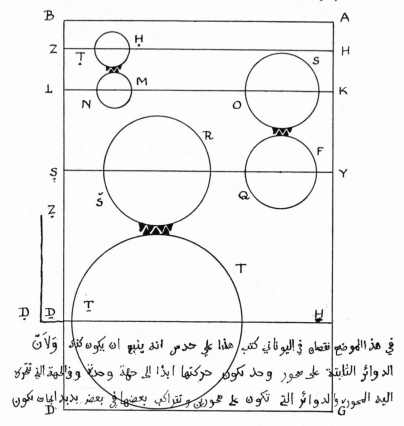

في هذا الموضع نقصان في اليوناني كتب / هذا على حدس انه ينبغ ان يكون كذا وَلَاّنَّ

الدوائر الثابتة على محور وحد نكون حركتها ابذا الى حهذ وحرنة وَفِيّالجهة الِيّ تَقرّيّ

اليه الحور؟ والدوائر التِّي نكون على محورين ونتراكبِ بعضها في بعض بدبد الجانب نكون

Fig. 5. The barulkos from the Mechanics 1:1.
The figure is drawn from a photographic copy of the Leiden MS p. 3. It is more of
a diagram than a figure. The teeth are shown as equilateral triangles, in accordance
with the best figures elsewhere. No attempt is made to make the ratios of the wheels
and cogs fit the text. See text p. 22 sq.

The Barulkos

The very first chapter of the Mechanics does certainly not belong where
it is found, and a closer study shows that it does not belong to the Mechanics at all.

Here is the text, and the figure from the Leiden MS; the figure in
the edition is an interpretation. See fig. 5.

> "We want to move the given weight by the given power by an arrangement
> of wheels with teeth. So we make a solid shape like a chest, and let there be in

its long, parallel sides parallel axles, and their distances are such that the teeth of one of them engage the teeth of the other, in the way we are going to explain. Let the shape be the chest marked ABǦD, and let there be placed in it an axle moving easily, that is HZ, and let there be fastened on it a toothed wheel, and that is the wheel ḤṬ, and let its diameter be for example five times the diameter of the axle HZ. Now, to use our construction as an example, let us make the burden we want to lift one thousand talents, and the moving power five talents; I mean that the man or youth who moves it is some one who can lift five talents by himself without any engine. Now if we pass the rope which is tied to the burden through a hole in the side AB so that it is wound round the axle HZ, then by the turning of the wheel ḤṬ and by the winding of the rope the burden will be lifted; and for the moving of the wheel ḤṬ a power of two hundred talents is necessary, because the diameter of the wheel is five times the diameter of the axle according to our supposition, and this has been made clear in the proofs of the five powers; but we haven't got a power of two hundred talents and so the wheel will not be turned. So we make another axle parallel to the axle HZ, and that is the axle KL, with a toothed wheel fixed on it, and this wheel is the wheel MN. And the wheel ḤṬ should also have teeth, engaging with the teeth of the wheel MN. And on the axle KL there should be fixed another wheel, and that is SO, whose diameter should be five times the diameter of MN; then there will be needed to lift the burden by means of the wheel SO a power of forty talents, because a fifth of two hundred talents is forty talents. So again we engage with the wheel SO another wheel, and that is the wheel FQ, fixed on another axle, and that is the axle YṢ. And on this axle another wheel is fixed, whose diameter is five times the diameter of FQ, and that is the wheel RŠ, and the power that moves the burden by the point RŠ will be eight talents; but the power that we are supposed to have is only five talents. So we make another toothed wheel and that is the wheel TṬ, and its diameter should be twice that of the diameter of the wheel RŠ, and it is fixed on another axle, and that is the Axle ḤD, and the wheel TṬ needs a power of four talents, and the power supposed for us is five talents, so that there is in this power a surplus of one talent which is used if perhaps there should be a resistance from the wheels.

It is clear from our description that when the mover moves the wheel TṬ, the axle ḤD will turn, and by its turning the wheel RŠ turns, and so also the axle YṢ turns, and the wheel FQ turns, and the wheel SO turns with it; and so the axle KL turns, and the wheel MN turns, and the wheel ḤṬ turns, and so the axle HZ turns, and the rope is wound round the axle and the burden is lifted; and so we have lifted by a power of five talents a burden to the amount of a thousand talents, by means of the engine which we have described; and that was what was to be proved. Note: It is necessary to prolong the axle ḌH towards Ḍ and to fix on it a stick ḌẒ of the same length as half of the diameter of the wheel TṬ or more; but Allah is the one who knows."

The note is found in the Leiden MS only, and the stick ḌẒ seems to have been added with a writing pen, not drawn in the same very fine line as the rest of the drawing.

The construction is very clear, but it is obvious that it is at fault in the last transmission, since the wheel TT should not be twice the wheel RŠ, but twice a cogwheel engaging RŠ. The drawing shows the wrong construction; but the description of the working of the engine says that the wheel TT is turned, and so the axle H̱Ḏ is turned, and by its turning the wheel RŠ turns, which implies a cogwheel on H̱Ḏ to engage RŠ. But it is not possible to correct the text by merely fitting in some such lines as: "Then we make another axle, H̱Ḏ, with a toothed wheel WX engaging the teeth of the wheel RŠ, and we fix on this axle a wheel TT, whose diameter should be twice that of the wheel WX ..." because no cog-wheel is mentioned in the description of the working, either.

Another queer thing is that the drawing is upside down, since the rope has to pass through a hole in the side AB.

The same engine, described partly in the very same words, is found in Heron's Dioptra, ch. 37 (50, 51), where it is also rather out of place. Here is the description; see fig. 6.

"To move the given weight by the given power by a combination of toothed wheels. Let there be made a framework like a chest; in the long and parallel sides there should be placed axles parallel to each other, so much apart that the toothed wheels fixed on them come near to each other and engage, as we are going to describe. Let the chest in question be ABΓΔ, in which there is placed an axle, as said, turning easily, the EZ. Fixed to this let there be a toothed wheel HΘ, which could have, for instance, five times the diameter of the axle EZ. And so as to make the contrivance serve for an example, let the weight to be moved be one thousand talents, and let the moving power be 5 talents, that is, the moving man or slave should be one who can move by himself without any engine 5 talents. Now if the ropes tied to the burden are passed through a ⟨hole⟩ in the side AB and wound round the axle EZ, ⟨when the wheel HΘ is turned⟩ the ropes from the burden will be wound up and the weight will be moved; but to move the wheel HΘ ⟨we need⟩ a power of more than two hundred talents, because the diameter of the wheel, according to our supposition, ⟨is⟩ five times the diameter of the axle, for this has been proved in the proofs about the 5 powers. But we ⟨do not⟩ have the power of two hundred talents, but five. So let there be another axle ⟨parallel⟩ to EZ, the KΛ, on which there is fixed a toothed wheel MN. The wheel HΘ is also toothed, so that it engages the teeth of the wheel MN. On the same axle KΛ there is fixed a wheel Ξ ⟨O⟩, which also has the five-fold diameter of the wheel MN. Because of this any one wanting to move the weight by means of the wheel ΞO will need to have a power of 40 talents, since one fifth of 200 talents is 40 talents. So there must again be placed along ⟨the toothed wheel ΞO⟩ another toothed wheel ⟨ΠP, and there should be⟩ fixed to the toothed wheel ΠP another wheel ⟨ΣT⟩ which has also a diameter five times that of the wheel ΠP. The cor⟨responding power⟩ of the wheel ΣT is one of a weight of 8 talents; but the available power has been assumed for us to be

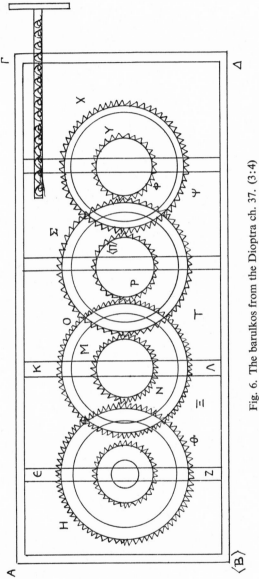

Fig. 6. The barulkos from the Dioptra ch. 37. (3:4)

The figure is taken from the Mynas Codex, fol. 82r. The letters B, Ϛ, ϛ are not found in the figure. The cog-wheel on the axle EZ is quite superfluous; the inner circle showing the diameter of the drum for the rope is all that is necessary. No attempt has been made to make the ratio of the wheels and pinions fit the text; the wheels are some 45 mm in diameter, the pinions 20 mm. See the text p. 24 sqq.

5 talents. So also another toothed wheel, YΦ, should be placed along the toothed wheel ΣT; fixed on the axle of this wheel YΦ should be a toothed wheel XΨ, whose diameter should have the ratio to the diameter of the wheel YΦ as eight talents to the given power of 5 talents. When this has been prepared, if we imagine the chest ABΓΔ placed on high, and we tie the weight to the axle EZ, and the pulling power to the wheel XΨ, neither side will go downwards, even if the axles are turning easily and the engagement of the wheels is fitted nicely, but the power will balance the weight as in a balance. But if we add a little more weight to one of them, the side where the weight is added will sink and go downwards, so that if just the weight of, say, one mina is added to the power of five talents, it will overcome the weight and pull it. In stead of this addition there may be placed on the wheel a screw whose thread fits into the teeth of the wheel, turning easily on pivots in round holes, one of which pivots should stick out outside the chest by the side ΓΔ where is the screw; this projecting end should be made square and be provided with a handle Cς, which you can grasp and turn and so turn the screw and the wheel XΨ, and so also YΦ, which is fixed to it. Hereby also ΣT, which engages it, is turned, and ΠP, which is fixed to it, and ΞO, which engages it, and MN, fixed to it; and HΘ, which engages it, and so also the axle EZ, which is fixed to it, and the ropes from the burden, which are wound round it, will move the weight. That it will move it is evident from the addition to the power of that of the handle, which describes a circle greater than that of the circumference of the screw; for it has been proved that greater circles conquer smaller circles when they turn on the same centre."

The figure is copied from the Mynas Codex in Paris (50). The text of the MS is a little defective, but the corrections by the editor, Hermann Schöne, are obviously right.

It is clear that we have here two different versions of the same engine. In the first part, the Arabic and the Greek texts are the same, almost word for word; but towards the end, the Greek text introduces a screw where the Arabic text has none. But furthermore it is evident that the Arabic version is defective, not only because, as I have explained, there is lacking a cog-wheel to transmit the power from the last axle to the one before it, but also because there are no means of turning the axle. The note in the Leiden MS supplies this missing element; but that note I take to be an insertion by the owner of the MS, because Heron himself would hardly have added "but Allah is the one who knows" or words to that effect; also the addition to the figure is made by another pen.

Another difference is that in the Arabic version we add at once a surplus of power to raise the burden; in the Greek version the power is first made to balance the burden, then something is added to lift it.

This is further complicated by a remark in the Leiden MS, a remark which the editor, Nix, has not printed in the text, though he has translated it on p. XXIX. It is found just below the figure, and it runs: "Here there is a lacuna in the Greek text; this is written on the supposition that it must be so." These words take up almost the whole of the first line just below the drawing; see fig. 5. The last word in the line وذلك is the first word of chapter 2 in MS C; MS K has first the heading: "About the wheels". The MS K has another remark, not printed, but translated by Nix on p. XXIX: "This manuscript is free from the lacuna which is found in others."

Nix takes these remarks as referring to the beginning of the real text, that is chapter 2, and wonders what may have been found in the Greek original, for nothing seems to be lacking. I prefer to take it as referring to the preceding chapter, as a remark by some scribe who has found the description of the engine defective: "There is something missing here; at least it looks like it to me." The writer in MS K has compared his copy with other copies and has found no lacuna, and he has said so.

In the edition, Nix has marked the words والله اعلم, "but Allah knows best" with "L om." Now MS B lacks the first few pages and does not begin till chapter 4; and for the whole note we read "CK om.", that is, the note is found in L only. As a matter of fact my photocopy shows the words plainly in the MS L. This is not the only intimation that the critical apparatus of Nix is not always fully reliable.

We may note that the author does not know here how to compute the effect of the screw. He only takes into account the difference in radius between the handle and the screw itself; the fact that the screw will turn the wheel tooth by tooth, which gives it such an enormous power, is not regarded at all. By the use of the screw most of the gear wheels would in fact be made quite superfluous. But in the Dioptra itself, where Heron uses a chain of screws and wheels for his hodometer, see p. 159 sqq., he knows quite well how to compute the ratio. This may mean that this addition to the engine was not made by Heron himself.

And now for the question: what is this thing? That it is not a displaced chapter from the Mechanics is easily seen, because a corresponding chapter is found in its place, 2:21, and is quite different, though it is obvious that it has served as a source for this engine; the "proofs of the five powers" quoted both in the Arabic and the Greek version are found in the 2. Book of the Mechanics, too.

In Pappos we have direct evidence that this engine was made by

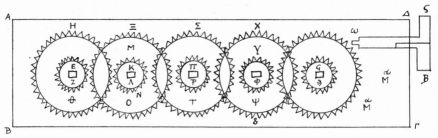

Fig. 7. The barulkos from Pappos, p. 1060 sqq. (3:4)
The figure is taken from the Vatican MS. See text p. 27 sqq.

Heron and called a *barulkos*, that is an engine for lifting heavy burdens. He has discussed the problem of moving a given weight on an inclined plane by a given power, and goes on (p. 1060):

> "The same theory applies to the work of moving a given weight by a given power; this was found out by Archimedes, who is said thereupon to have exclaimed: "Give me somewhere to stand, and I shall move the earth." Heron of Alexandria has shown quite clearly in the so-called Barulkos how this may be contrived, using as a basis that which he had proved in his Mechanics, where he also discusses the 5 powers, that is the wedge and the lever and the screw and the pulley and the axle in the wheel (i.e. the windlass) by which a given weight is moved by a given power. In the Barulkos he moves the given weight by a given power through a combination of toothed wheels, where the diameter of the wheel has a ratio to that of the axle as 5 to 1, and the given weight is one thousand talents, the given power 5 talents."

Pappos then goes on to describe a similar engine, using the ratio 2:1 for his wheels and pinions. See fig. 7. He ends by fitting a screw, as in ch. 37 of the Dioptra, and he gives the same explanation of the working of the screw, adding a few words of his own:

> "That it will be moved is evident, since there is added the extra power of the handle, which describes a circle larger than the circumference of the screw, for it has been proved in the work "On Balances" by Archimedes and in the Mechanics of Philon and Heron, that the larger circles overcome the smaller circles, when their revolution takes place round the same centre."

From this is would seem reasonable to conclude that this engine was constructed by Heron and named the *barulkos*; except that, as I have suggested, the screw may have been added by a later hand.

This latter assumption is to a small extent supported by a study of the figures.

The barulkos of the Arabic version, fig. 5, is drawn very schematically, though quite plain to the intelligent reader. The axles are shown as single lines; the wheels are just circles, except where they engage; here the teeth are shown as small, black triangles, fitting nicely together. The chest consists of single lines.

In the figure from the Dioptra, fig. 6, the sides of the chest are shown to have a certain thickness, and so are the axles; the wheels and pinions are shown in pairs on their axles, only the axle is made parallel to the wheels. This is a concession to the scribe; he should be able to render the drawing by rule and compasses. The teeth on the wheels are just a zig-zag line drawn free-hand; and since all the wheels have the same diameter, like the pinions, the teeth engage far more than they should. The screw, which is indicated by curlicues inside two parallel lines, does not engage the last wheel at all. On the first axle, EZ, a cog-wheel is shown; this is an error, since this should be the smooth drum for the rope. This cog-wheel does not engage the next wheel; a smaller circle inside it seems to indicate the drum.

In Pappos, fig. 7, the drawing has taken a step further. The chest, it is true, consists of single lines; but the axles are shown as squares in the middle of the cog-wheels. The same diameter is used for all the wheels and pinions respectively; but the teeth do not engage anywhere. The pinions have 20 teeth (one has got only 19), and the wheels 40 teeth, in accordance with the text. The screw has a fine pivot, but it is shown as a plain cylinder, and it does not attempt to engage anything. Through its head there is a queer line which I cannot explain.

The first pinion, which is quite superfluous, is found here also, but the circle for the drum, shown in fig. 6, is left out.

That this drawing is derived from fig. 6 seems quite evident; and that that again comes from fig. 5 is also clear. Yet the difference can hardly be accepted as proof that Heron, who made fig. 5, did not also make fig. 6. For if we compare this with the figure for the same engine in the Mechanics, 2:21, fig. 29a, we shall find that this is like fig. 6 in several respects. The axle or drum carrying the burden is shown parallel to the wheel on it; the wheels and pinions have zig-zag teeth. There can be no doubt that fig. 6 has come about as a combination of fig. 5 and fig. 29a. But both fig. 5 and fig. 29a are undoubtedly by Heron himself; and fig. 5 must be later than fig. 29a, since "the proof of the five powers" is mentioned in 1:1, to which it belongs.

The explanation might be that fig. 5 represents Heron's first attempt at drawing the chest with the axles and the wheels, a much more intricate task than that of drawing the single succession of wheels shown in fig. 29a. It will be found that fig. 29a does not show a real engine, only a theoretical solution of a problem; the supports for the axles are mentioned only when the construction is changed from toothed wheels to plain drums and ropes. See p. 83.

On the other hand, the drawing of the screw in the Dioptra is without counterpart in the Mechanics, where the screw is generally shown as two parallel lines with oblique cross lines; in MS B it is sometimes shown just as two parallel lines. Exceptions are fig. 18a, from MS L, where there is a row of double triangles across the axle, and the same figure in MS B, fig. 18b, with one single and one double figure of eight round the axle. The two screws in fig. 28a, looking like triangles put together, I regard as later additions; see p. 78.

This may raise the question whether fig. 6 was indeed made by Heron.

This analysis of the drawings only confirms the hypothesis that the screw is a later addition to the *barulkos*; but the question of whether it was added by Heron himself or not is still open.

For a discussion of the entirely different drawing of the same subject in the ships' hodometer see p. 167 sqq. and fig. 63a.

To return to Pappos, he mentions the Barulkos once more, in the Excerpts from Heron (p. 1114):

> "So much about the Barulkos; the exposition of the above mentioned 5 powers from Heron we shall write out more shortly for the reminding of the students ..."

Hultsch in his edition separates this chapter from the preceding text by three asterisks and adds, in the Latin translation, the superscription: "Excerpts from Heron's Mechanics", thus indicating that this text is not by Pappos himself, and that it does not continue the preceding text.

In a paper written in 1877, before the Arabic text of Heron's Mechanics was made known (72), Hultsch has collected all the information about the Mechanics he has found in Pappos. He comes to the conclusion that Pappos Book 8 is not from Pappos's hand alone; it is strongly interpolated by excerpts from Heron, both in the introduction and among the other chapters. This interpolator, whose style is inferior to that of Pappos, is an intelligent man, and one whose quotations may be trusted to be correct.

As for the chapter 52: "So much about the Barulkos", Hultsch contends that it could not have been placed in this connexion by a man in his right mind. But it is not quite certain that he is right.

The preceding chapters, 45–51 (25–30) ,contain propositions 20–24. Of these prop. 20–21 show how two toothed wheels with 60 and 40 teeth respectively are made to engage with each other, and what their relative speeds will be; prop. 22 shows that the ratio of the circumference of two circles is the same as the ratio of their diameters; prop. 23 shows how to construct a toothed wheel with a given number of teeth to fit another toothed wheel with a given number of teeth; and prop. 24 undertakes to describe how to make a screw to fit the teeth of a given wheel, while it really describes the converse process: how to make a wheel to fit a given screw.

But if you want to construct a *barulkos* as described by Heron and Pappos, these are the operations you will have to perform: to make gear-wheels in a known ratio, and to make a wheel and a screw that fit together. In the 2. Book of the Mechanics we have in ch. 16 the directions of how to make a screw, different in wording from that of Pappos prop. 24; and in ch. 18 the explanation of how the screw and the gear-wheel work together; the construction of the wheel to fit the screw is found in Book 1:19; but the chapters in Pappos are not taken directly from the Mechanics. But towards the end of ch. 50 the Mechanics are quoted, and ch. 51 is an abbreviated rendering of Heron's ch. 18.

From this it seems reasonable to conclude that Pappos ch. 45–50 belong with the Barulkos, and that they and ch. 51 were added by Pappos or the interpolator from Heron's Mechanics. There is still a long way to go from the last chapter of the Barulkos, 24, to ch. 45; but the occurrence of the word Barulkos in ch. 52 has been explained. We can now imagine the Barulkos as a short work by Heron himself, containing the description of the engine to lift 1000 talents by means of a power of 5 talents by a combination of gear-wheels.

Against this Nix has set up another hypothesis (86), to wit that the Barulkos is the proper name for Heron's Mechanics. His main argument is that Qusṭâ ibn Lûqâ translates the title as "Heron's book on the lifting of heavy burdens", which is quite a good translation of the word "Barulkos" into Arabic, but not at all of the word "Mechanics"; when Pappos speaks of the Mechanics, Nix refers to the rather careless way in which Pappos treats the titles of other works.

Still, I do not think that Nix is right. In the first place because the word Barulkos, which means an engine for lifting heavy burdens, is not a very probable title for a work containing a large amount of both theoretical and practical knowledge. Next I should like to call attention to the place in Pappos quoted p. 28, where the Barulkos is quoted as something distinct from the Mechanics. When Pappos wrote his book, and when the interpolator put in fragments from Heron here and there, the Mechanics and the Barulkos were two separate works. But the MS from which Quṣṭâ ibn Lûqâ translated the Mechanics contained the first part of the Barulkos as its chapter 1. If the superscription of this spurious chapter was "Heron's Barulkos", no wonder if the translator took it to be the title of the whole work. He could do this all the more confidently because his translation "The book on lifting of heavy objects" is quite a good title for the whole work.

As for the Barulkos, I take it to be just a theoretical solution of the given problem; we shall find several of the same kind in the 2. Book of the Mechanics. How and why it has escaped and started to live a life of its own I cannot say. In the Mechanics, 2:21, quoted on p. 83, we learn that if we do not want to use gear-wheels, we can use ropes instead. This was the actual method, as described by Vitruvius Book 10, ch. 2, par. 5–7. But nowhere do we find gear-wheels used, except in water-mills, where the power was enormous, and in the Antikythera instrument, where no great power was needed. It is rather significant that there is not a single cog-wheel in Heron's Automatic Theatre, nor in the limb-setting engines in Oreibasios. Gear-wheels were used fro lifting burdens in theory only.

The Mechanics

Once we have set this unexpected introductory chapter aside, the first Book of the Mechanics runs on quite smoothly.

The whole book is meant as an introduction to the study of mechanics, which is the science of haulage and lifting. So the student first learns about the working of wheels, that is in ch. 2–6. It is the same theme as in Aristoteles's Mechanical Problems, only here gear-wheels are used for illustration; we learn how the wheels behave when they engage each other, when they are of equal or unequal size, and when they are sitting on the same axle.

In ch. 7 Heron tackles the problem that puzzled Aristoteles, see p. 14. Two wheels of different size are fixed on the same axle. If they make one revolution, rolling along the circumference of the larger wheel, the smaller wheel will travel the same distance, which is larger than its circumference; if the smaller wheel does the rolling, the larger wheels travels a distance shorter than its circumference in one revolution. Heron explains it quite simply: one wheel rolls, the other is both slipping and rolling.

Ch. 8 gives the parallelogram of the forces, as in Aristoteles Problem 23.

Ch. 9–19 explain how to construct similar figures, in greater or smaller scale. Ch. 9 deals with plane figures. If we want to construct two plane figures with their areas in a given proportion, say a:b, we construct a mean proportional between a and b: a:c = c:b; then we have: ab = c²; a²b = c²a; a:b = a²:c². If we use the proportion a:c in all the lines of the two figures, their area will be in the proportion a:b. How we find the mean proportional Heron does not say; he takes it for granted that his students know how to do it from Euclid 6:11.

Ch. 10 shows that in order to construct a cube in a given proportion to another cube we have to find two mean proportionals between the sides.

Ch. 11 shows how this is done.

This is a solution of the famous Delian Problem, the reduplication of the cube; it has often been discussed (125).

So far we have learnt to enlarge or reduce similar, regular plane figures and bodies.

Ch. 12, 13, and 14 show how irregular plane figures are treated. If a line is turned round a point A, any two points on it, B and C, will describe lines in the proportion AB to AC.

Ch. 15 describes an instrument to help us in this work. It is a sort of pantograph, built on the principle studied in ch. 7.

"⟨15⟩ And let us now prove how to make a figure similar to the known plane figure in the given ratio by means of an instrument. We make two wheels on the same centre, fixed to it, and provided with teeth, moving on a single axle in the plane where is the figure we want to copy; and the ratio of one wheel to the other should be the given ratio. And let there be by each of the wheels a rod with teeth on that side, and let the teeth be engaged with the teeth of the wheels. And let these two rods be in a furrow like a canal in another rod which turns on the axle of the wheels by a round hole. And let there be on the ends of the toothed rods marks for the lines of the similar figures, and let these marks lie on a straight line with the centre of the wheels. And so that both of them must move on a straight line with the centre of the wheels, and the three marks work together in unison, and must needs be on a single straight line, we must make

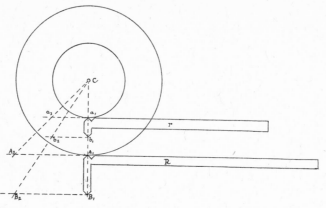

Fig. 8a illustrates Heron 1:15; it is a diagram to show the position of the marks on the racks of the pantograph. See text p. 34 sq.

the marks that are on the toothed rods † a distance of the rods the amount of the distance that is for the centre of each of the wheels. † Then we turn it so that it reaches the plane in which we want to make the similar figures. And if someone draws out a mark and places it on the line by which the figure is contained, and if the other is distant from it so that the distance which is between it and the centre of the wheels is to the distance which is between it and the other mark like the relation of the diameters of the toothed wheels to one another, and the rod in which is the furrow like a canal is curved a little, so that the mark that is on the line which we have mentioned runs on this line, then the other mark draws the figure similar to the first figure and draws it also in the known ratio, because the toothed wheels have this ratio to one another."

The expression that the two wheels are "fixed to the centre" means that they are fastened concentrically together.

Between the † † the text is not in order. Nix has corrected it and translates: "Müssen wir die Merkpunkte auf den gezahnten Linealen so weit von dem Mittelpunkte der Scheiben entfernt machen, als die kürzeste Entfernung des Mittelpunktes beider Scheiben von den Rändern der Lineale beträgt."

If we consider the theory of the instrument, we shall find, as shown in fig. 8a, that if the racks are just mathematical lines, and the rack r is moved so that a_1 falls on a_2, the rack R will be moved so that A_1 falls on A_2, and $\dfrac{a_1 a_2}{A_1 A_2} = \dfrac{Ca_1}{CA_2}$.

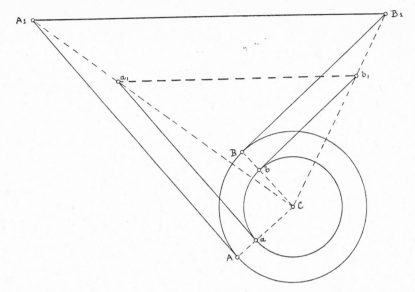

Fig. 8 b illustrates Heron 1:15; it is a diagram to show that the pantograph will work, in theory at least. See text p. 36.

But if we give the rods a thickness, and the mark on the rack r at b_1 moves to b_2, the mark on the rack R must be at B_1, so as to reach B_2,

when $\dfrac{b_1 b_2}{B_1 B_2} = \dfrac{Ca_1}{CA_1} = \dfrac{Cb_1}{CB_1}$; so what Heron is trying to say is that the two marks on the rods and the centre of the wheels will be kept on a straight line, if the distance from the centre to the two marks has the same proportion as the diameters of the wheels. But I cannot correct the text to mean this.

A "furrow like a canal" means a groove with a square cross-section. The two racks have to be guided in grooves in a holder turning on the same axle as the wheels. To make sure that the three cardinal points are on a straight line from the beginning, we make one side of the holder point towards the centre.

The marks on the racks must be on their ends. In the figure in MS B both racks have their ends bent at right angles to form pointers; in MS L only one rack is bent. If the points of the racks follow the rule laid down above, the shape of the rack has no importance for the theoretical efficiency of the instrument, but much for its practical use.

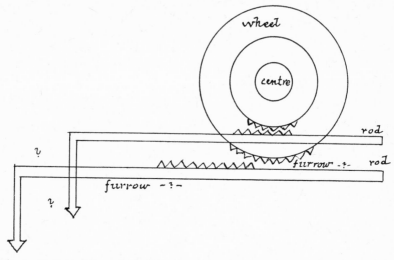

Fig. 8c illustrates Heron 1:15. It is taken from the MS B and shows the pantograph or copying instrument. The words on the figure are not written in the same hand as the text, and I have not been able to read all of them. See text p. 33 sqq.

Fig. 8b is a diagram to show that theoretically the instrument is in order. We want to make a figure similar to A_1B_1 in the ratio 3:2. We place the instrument, with the wheels in the ratio 3:2, at C, and pull out the outer rack till its mark touches A_1; the point of the inner rack will fall at a_1, and A_1, a_1, and C will be on a straight line. Then we turn the instrument round the point C and place the end of the outer rack at B_1, and mark b_1 at the point of the inner rack; once more the three points, B_1, b_1, and C fall on a straight line. Now to prove that

$$\frac{A_1B_1}{a_1b_1} = \frac{CA}{Ca} = \frac{3}{2}$$

From the triangle ACA_1, where $AA_1 \neq aa_1$, we find $\dfrac{CA}{Ca} = \dfrac{CA_1}{Ca_1}$

From the triangle BCB_1, where $BB_1 \neq bb_1$, we find $\dfrac{CB}{Cb} = \dfrac{CB_1}{Cb_1}$

but $CB = CA$, $Cb = Ca$, so $\dfrac{CA_1}{Ca_1} = \dfrac{CB_1}{Cb_1}$, and $\dfrac{A_1B_1}{a_1b_1} = \dfrac{CA_1}{Ca_1} = \dfrac{CA}{Ca}$

q.e.d.

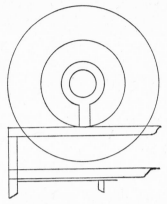

Fig. 8d illustrates Heron 1:15. This is the same figure as fig. 8c, but taken from the MS L. (3:4) See the text p. 33 sqq.

Fig. 8c shows the pantograph as figured in **MS B**. The two wheels on the same centre and the two racks with their bent ends are clearly shown; enough teeth are drawn on both racks and wheels to show what they are. The lettering is written very carelessly; I have made out only part of it.

Fig. 8d is taken from **MS L** and shows the same instrument. We recognize the two wheels on a common centre, to which is added the rod to contain the grooves for the racks; only it stops short at the first rack, and no grooves are seen. Of the two racks only one is bent, and no teeth are shown anywhere. All in all it is a very poor figure.

Ch. 16 teaches the student to transfer a given plane figure from one place to another. A circle is drawn inside the figure, and from its centre lines are drawn to all the angles of the figure. The circle is repeated in the new place for the figure; the intersections of the radial lines with the circle are marked, and all the points of the new figure can be constructed.

Ch. 17 tells us that for a spatial figure we have to use a sphere, but this is theory only.

Ch. 18 describes an instrument with which to make a copy of any irregular, spatial figure in a given proportion to the original.

"As for spatial figures, we construct them in this way. We take two plane boards of wood, which move along a line which they have in common, and this common line must be the same during every movement. And this can be obtained if

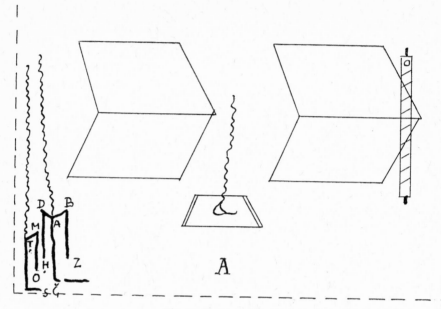

Fig. 9a illustrates Heron 1:18.

A is copied from the MS L.

B is my reconstruction of the rather cramped drawing of the two "Tau".

C is a diagram of the "Tau" as they must have looked. The letters do not correspond to those in the reconstruction by Nix; but the MS figure does not allow of any other distribution. See text p. 37 sqq.

the centres of the hinges on which the boards move are on this common line. And the size of the boards is determined by the size of the larger of the two similar figures. This is the work † and what is needed for it, that is what we are going to explain.

Let us take two iron figures that resemble the letter called Tau, and let the parts of each of them when stretched be similar. And let us bend their ends sharply, and let there be formed by this bending of both of them the shape of a triangle. And let the ratio of one of the spatial figures to the other be as the ratio of the cubes of the sides of the triangles. (See fig. 9a.) And let us imagine this with regard to the lines AB, AČ, AD; and the lines that have been bent are ČH, BZ, DḤ. And the other figure is the lines TK, TL, TM, and the lines that have been bent are KN, LS, MO. And let the similar triangles be ḤHZ, NOS. And let us mark on the line common to the two movable boards on one of the boards a figure similar in size and shape to the iron shape, and we draw along one side of the triangle a line parallel to the base of the triangle, so that it cuts off another triangle similar to the other triangle of iron which resembles the letter Tau. And let there be made fast on each of the two figures of Tau a rod of lead, and let its end be made quite pointed, so that if it is bent in any direction whatever and

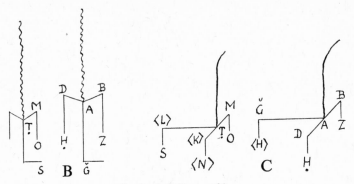

Fig. 9a B, C. Text p. 38.

let go, it will stay, that is, it will not quiver, just as it is with the leaden rods used
for human portraits. And the shape of the letter called Tau shall resemble the
tool called *galeagra*. And the boards we have described should be movable one
against the other in such a way that when the movement is stopped they stand
firm and do not wobble at all, like the crabs. This then is the construction of the
tool; and now we are going to describe its use. [One MS adds:] He says: and
this is by means of a screw, as it is shown in the drawing".

The place marked by a † is corrupt, but the meaning seems clear
if we compare it to the last sentence of the description: "This is the
construction of the tool, and now we are going to describe its use."

"The letter Tau". The text has: (two figures like), يسمى الذى الحرف,
هولاء. Carra de Vaux translates: "à la pince que l'on appelle chèlé".
But Nix points out that حرف cannot mean "pince", and that هولاء
cannot represent χηλή, "claw". He himself takes حرف in the ordinary
sense of "letter", and هولاء as "Ypsilon", where ه is the *spiritus lenis*
and و is the υ, while لاء represents the letter itself, Y; but he gives the
explanation with every reservation. I do not think that ه can represent
spiritus lenis, and the shape of the figures does not resemble an ypsilon,
they look like the letter T. So I suggest that the Greek text had τῷ
γράμματι τ, and that the translator has read τ as ταῦτα, and translated
it by هولاء, "these". But also this explanation is given with reservation.
"a rod of lead". Nix translates "ein Zinnstab"; رصاص means both tin
and lead, and lead seems better suited for the purpose.
"*galeagra*" means a cage; in the Mechanics 3:16, 17 it is used for a
wooden cage to contain olives to be pressed. I fail to see any likeness
in the two "giraffes" of this chapter.
"crab". سراطين The same word is used in 3:7 about a sort of claw for

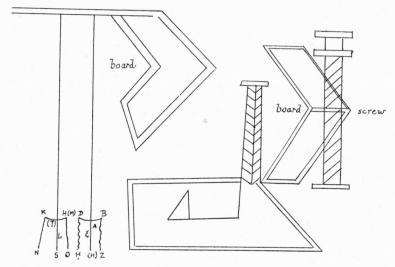

Fig. 9 b illustrates Heron 1:19; it is the same figure as fig. 9a, but taken from the MS B. (3:4) The two figures are discussed in the text p. 40–41.

hoisting stones. But if it is a translation of the Greek καρκίνος, it may mean a pair of compasses, which would give good sense.

"by means of a screw". The text has بكوكب, which Nix changes into بالالواح "about the boards"; the sense then becomes: "He says: and this about the boards is as it is shown in the drawing". But the MS B often has كوكب in stead of لولب; sometimes it is corrected كُوكب , sometimes not. So I make it: "by means of a screw". The drawings both in MS L and MS B show a screw very plainly to the right of the hinged boards; in the MS B it is marked by the word "screw", while the boards have "board". There is no structural connexion between the boards and the screw in either drawing. I do not know of a screw for adjusting compasses; but several gynecological *specula* adjusted by a screw are known from this time (35, 136).

Figs 9a and 9b show the drawings from the two MSS, L and B.

In Fig. 9a, A, from MS L, we see clearly on the right hand the hinged boards with the screw, which has two pivots and a hole, probably for turning it. Of its connexion with the boards we learn nothing. On the left we see the boards once more, and in the bottom left-hand corner are the two iron "Taus". B shows my reconstruction of these figures, and C shows how the two instruments must have looked.

I cannot explain the figure between the two sets of boards. The wriggly line must be one of the lead feelers, and so its foot should be the "Tau". The thing on which it stands should be a board, since it has a definite thickness, but the whole thing does not give any sense.

Turning to fig. 9b, from MS B, we recognize on the right hand the boards and the screw, which here has two disks on top and one below, for turning, or perhaps for connecting it with the boards. Two inscriptions show what they are. On the left is the board, very badly drawn, but marked "board", and then the two "Taus". That the letter H is written for M is a simple error of the scribe. The middle figure is quite puzzling; but it seems to me that it may have arisen from the middle figure in MS L or a common source. As it stands it is quite unintelligible.

"If we want to make a spatial figure similar to another, given spatial figure in a given ratio, we bring the surface of the spatial figure near to the figure Tau, so that it touches the points of the surface from all sides, and we bring in the same way the other figure resembling a Tau near the figure we are going to form, and if we want to make it larger than the given figure, we place the larger figure near the larger triangle, and the other one near the second one".

This means that if we want to enlarge, we measure the original with the smaller Tau, the copy with the larger Tau, and *vice versa*. The triangles are two triangles exactly like those drawn on the board; the original and the copy must be fixed in relation to these two triangles.

"And let it be that we want to make the copy in stone or wood or some other material, and we make on each body position marks; and let marks mentioned be placed on the bodies on corresponding places, and let us then make the other parts in the same way".

The meaning is quite plain: we select the salient points of the original, transfer them to the copy, and use them for getting the right shape. But the translator seems to have got his moods mixed.

"So that our explanation may be clear, let us assume that we want to form an eye on a human figure or on some other figure; we place the points of the Tau near the known figure, I mean the one that is given us and to which we want to make a similar shape, and we bend the point of the leaden rod which is on the Tau so that its point touches the eye that we want. Then we take away the Tau and place it on the triangle which is drawn on the board. Then we lower or raise the other board on which nothing is drawn, till the point of the rod touches it, by the lowering or lifting. Then we take away the Tau and draw two lines from the point marked by the leaden rod on the board to the two sides of the triangle on the line common to the two boards, and we take care that the two boards do not move in respect to one another. Next we draw from the other

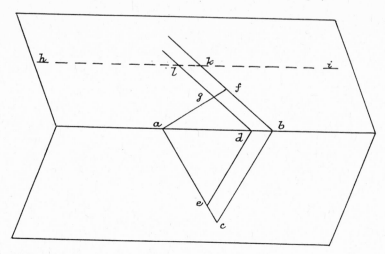

Fig. 10 illustrates Heron 1:18; it is a diagram showing how the drawing on the hinged
board is made by means of the parallel line h–i. See text p. 42–43.

point on the line that is in common to the two boards a line parallel to the larger
lines [sic] that are on the line parallel to the base, till it cuts the other line".

The text is not in order, but the meaning is clear; see fig. 10. *abc*
is the triangle for the larger Tau on the fixed board, *ade* that for the
smaller Tau. On the moving board *f* is the point marked by the larger
Tau; the lines *fa* and *fb* have been drawn. To find *g* we draw the line
dg parallel to *bf*.

"Then we take the other Tau and place the sharp ends of the teeth that were
bent on the triangle that is on the board, the one that is similar to the triangle
made by the ends of these parts, and we bend the leaden rod till it touches the
point marked by the parallel line on the other board; and we take away the Tau
and place it on the marks on the shape that is not yet made. And that point
which the end of the rod touches on the body, that point is placed on the place
of the eye of the copy corresponding to the place on which the first rod was bent.
And in the same way we bend the rod on the other remaining parts and mark
the corresponding points on the stone. Then we construct the surface from the
given points, and these are the points by which the shape will be similar to the
first shape and it will be in the given proportion to it. As for the parallel line
mentioned it will be easy to draw it on the other board, if we draw on the board
a line somewhere parallel to the common line".

Nix regards this last sentence as superfluous and quite unintelligible.
But if in fig. 10 we draw the line *hi* parallel to *ab*, the line *dg* is very

easy to draw if we make *kl* equal to *bd*, and so for any other oblique, parallel line we may want to make. To me this remark suggests that Heron has actually used the instrument.

"That the figures made in this way are similar is evident, for they belong to similar pyramids in similar positions, their bases consisting of the triangles made by the Tau on the bodies and their tops consisting of the points which the ends of the rods have marked on each of the bodies. And that they have the given proportion to one another is evident, because the proportion of the pyramids by which the figures are made are in three times the proportion of the proportional sides, for the sides of the similar triangles were supposed to be that way. And so the bodies have this known proportion to one another."

Three times the proportion means the cubical proportion.

Ch. 19 goes on to describe the way of copying the back of a figure, and how to make inverted copies.

Next comes a description of how to make a cog-wheel with a given number of teeth to fit a given screw. This part of the chapter might be displaced from Book. 2, but for the apology in the first passage.

"And how we make on a wheel teeth in a given number and make it fit a given screw, that is what we are going to explain, because it is of great use for what we are going to teach later on". (See fig. 11). "Let the screw be along AB and let the screw thread be lentil-shaped, and let the distance of this screw thread be of the size ǦD, DH, HZ, and let these three lines be equal. And now we want to make a wheel with twenty teeth to fit the screw thread which is on the screw. So we draw a circle of any size we like, and that is the circle ḤṬK, and let its centre be at the point L, and we divide the circumference of the circle into twenty equal parts, and let one of those twenty parts be the arc ḤṬ."

Nix inserts a "not" before "lentil-shaped" and takes the screw-furrow and the teeth to be square. But that would mean that the wheel must be divided into forty parts.

"And we join the points ḤṬ, LṬ, LḤ, and we make the line ḤM equal to one of the lines ǦD, DH, HZ; and we draw from the point L a line parallel to the line ḤṬ, and that is the line LN, and let this line be equal to ḤM, and we join the points MN by the line MN. And this will cut the line LṬ, and let the intersection be at the point S; and we draw with L as centre and LS as radius a circle SOF; and it is evident for us that the arc SO is one part out of twenty parts of the circle SOF, since the arc ḤṬ is one part out of twenty of the circumference of the circle ḤṬK, and the circle SOF is the inner circle. And this is the circle we have to define, if we prolong the line LS by a line segment equal to the depth of the screw thread and trace with the whole length of the line segment a circle with L as centre. And we must know that the parts outside the circle must fit into the depths of the screw thread, because SO is equal to HD; but

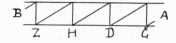

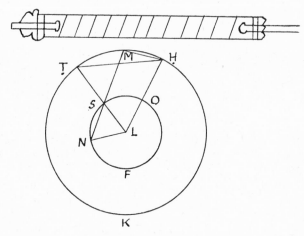

Fig. 11 illustrates Heron 1:19; it shows how to make a cog-wheel to fit a given screw. The figure is taken from the MS B; it is not found in the MS L.
Above the MS figure I have shown how the screw must have been lettered. See text p. 43 sq. The figure is not quite correct; the line NSM is not parallel to LOH, because the scribe has placed the point M on the circle in stead of on the Line ḤṬ. In fact, the chord ḤM should not have been drawn at all.

really it does not fit, because the distance of the outer screw thread is equal to the distance of the inner screw thread, but in the teeth the distance between their outer tops is greater than the distance which is between their inner bottoms; and because the difference in this is not perceptible, it will cause no hindrance to the working. And also the grooves of the teeth that are on the rim of the wheel must not be at right angles such as we make the teeth of wheels that have to fit one another, but we make them at a slant so that the teeth may fit exactly anywhere on the screw furrow. And we shall succeed in this if we divide the circle on the side of the wheel into twenty equal parts and draw a line from one of the divisions along the same slant as the screw threads, and divide the other side of the wheel in an equal number of parts, and join these divisions by lines on the rim of the circumference of the wheel. Then we cut out the teeth, and the screw threads will correspond, and the teeth of the wheel will fit them. And about how the slant must be of the teeth that are on the circumference of the wheel during the turning, and ⟨how⟩ we make the slant of the teeth that are on the rim of the circumference of the wheel to fit into the screw furrow, that is what we are now going to explain."

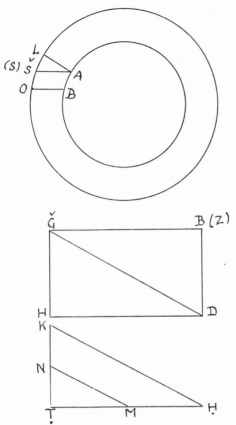

Fig. 12 illustrates Heron 1:19; it shows how to make the cogs oblique to suit the screw. It is taken from the MS L; it is not found in the MS B.
Two of the letters do not fit the text. The space between the two circles represents the felloe of the cog-wheel. See text p. 44 sqq.

The "how" seems necessary. Nix takes the sentence as a parenthesis: "– for we make the slant of the teeth on the rim of the wheel so that they engage the furrow of the screw –".

"Let us imagine a wheel, and let the distance of one of the teeth be the line AB, and let the screw furrow that is in the screw be the line ǦD between two lines parallel to the base of the cylinder, and these are ǦZ, HD". (See fig. 12). " And let us imagine two lines at right angles to one another, and they are the lines ḤṬ, ṬK; and let the line DH be equal to the line ṬḤ, and the line ǦH be equal to the line ṬK, and let us join the points ḤK. And we draw from the point A a line at right angles to the wheel on the rim of the wheel, and that is the line AL, and the line segment AL is the thickness of the wheel; and let the line ṬM be equal to the line AL; and we draw the line MN parallel to the line ḤK and let the line LS be equal to the line ṬN on the other circumference of the wheel, and we join the points AS and we divide the circumference LS from the point S by the number of teeth, and let SO be one dividing point, and we join OB, and the groove of the teeth will be on the two lines AS, BO, and the rest of the teeth let it be like that."

In ch. 20 we come to the theory of mechanics in general.

"There are those that think that burdens lying flat are moved by an equal power ⟨only⟩, wherein they hold wrong opinions. So let us explain that burdens placed in the way described are moved by a power smaller than any known power, and we shall explain the reason why this is not evident in practice. Let us imagine a burden lying flat, and let it be regular, smooth and let its parts be coherent with each other. And let the surface on which the burden lies be able to be inclined to both sides, I mean to the right and the left. And let it be inclined first towards the right. Then it it evident to us that the supposed burden will incline towards the right side, because the nature of the burdens is to move downwards, if nothing holds them and hinders them from the movement; and again if the inclined side is lifted to a horizontal position and comes into equilibrium, the burden will come to rest in this position. And if it is inclined to the other side, I mean to the left side, the burden will again sink towards the inclined side, even if the inclination is very small, and the burden will need no power to move it, but will need a power to hold it so that it does not move. And if the burden is again in equilibrium without inclination to any side, then it will stay there although there is no power to hold it, and it will not cease being at rest, until the surface inclines to one side or another; and then it will incline towards that side. And the burden that is ready to go to every side, how can it fail to need to move it a very small power of the size of the power that will incline it? And so the burden is moved by any small power."

Chapter 21 carries on the argument.

"The waters that are on a surface that is not inclined will not flow, but remain without inclining to either side. But if the slightest inclination comes to the water, then all of it will incline towards that side, till not the smallest part of the water is staying on it (the surface), unless there are hollows in the surface, and a small part of the water stays in the bottom of the hollows, as it happens often in the vessels. And this happens to the water because its parts are not bound together strong in dissolution."

The text does not seem quite in order; "bound together with a strong binding", i.e. "strongly", is expected.

"As for the bodies that are coherent, since by nature they are not smooth on their surfaces and not easily made smooth, it happens from the roughness of the bodies that they support each other, and in this way it happens that they lean upon each other like the teeth, and they are hindered (from moving) in this way, because when they (the teeth) are many and they are all joined together against each other, it is necessary to get together a great power."

Here also the text seems to fail. Does it mean that a great power is necessary to move the bodies? or that the teeth exert a great power of resistance?

"But from the experiment people got knowledge; they placed under the tortoises pieces of wood whose surfaces were cylindrical and did not touch more than a small part of the ground, and so only very little roughness met it. And they use poles and they move the burdens on them easily, even though the weight of the tools is added to the burden."

The "tortoises" are sleds for dragging loads; "poles" is the translation of σκυτάλη, which may mean either a handspake or, as here, a roller. For the sense "wheel-tooth" see p. 202.

"And some people put on the ground planed boards because of their smoothness and smear them with grease, because the roughness that is on them is made smooth, and so they move the burdens with small power. As for the cylinders, if they are heavy and lie on the ground, so that the ground does not touch more than one line of them, they are moved easily, and so also the balls; and we have already talked about that."

"⟨22⟩. If we want to lift the burden to a place higher up, we shall want for this a power equal to the burden. Let us imagine a tackle-block hung up, moveable at right angles to the horizontal plane, and let it be easily moveable round a centre on an axle. And let there be round the rim of its circumference a rope, one of whose ends is tied to the load, and the other end is by the drawing power. Now I contend that this burden is moved by a power equal to it. Now if there is not at the other end of the rope a power, but there is another burden tied to it, then it is evident for us that if the burdens are equal, then the block will not incline to any side, and the first burden will not overcome the second burden that is tied on, nor will the burden overcome the load, since the second burden tied on is equal to the first load. But if there is added to the burden some small amount, then the second burden will be drawn upwards, and so the power that moves the load, if it is greater than the load, will overcome it and move it, unless there arises friction in the turning of the block or stiffness in the ropes, so that a hindrance for the movement comes from this."

"⟨23⟩. As for the burdens that are on the sloping surfaces, their nature is to incline downwards also, as is the movement of all bodies. And if it is not as we have said, then we have to imagine also here the cause which we have mentioned above". (Thas is, if the bodies stay on the slope, there must be some such cause as friction or the like). "Now let us imagine that we want to move some burden on a sloping plane upwards, and let its surface be smooth and even, and so also the part of the burden on which it rests. For this we have to place some

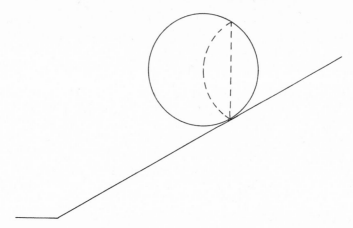

Fig. 13 is a diagram to illustrate 1:23, a cylinder on a slope. No figure is found in the MSS. See text p. 47 sqq.

power or some burden on the other side first, to overcome the burden, I mean, to balance it, so that there the increase in it shall overcome the burden and lift it upwards. So that our explanation may be proved to be true, we will explain it for a given cylinder. Because the cylinder does not touch the ground with a great part of itself, it is its nature to roll downwards. Now let us imagine a plane going through the line that touches the surface and at right angles to that surface, and it is evident to us that this plane will pass through the axis of the cylinder and divide it into two halves, because if there is a circle and a line touches it and a line is drawn from the point of touch at right angles, then this line will go through the centre of the circle; and we also draw through this line, I mean the line on the cylinder, another plane at right angles to the horizon, and this will not be the plane first drawn, and it will divide the cylinder into two unequal parts, of which the smaller will be towards the upper part, and the greater towards the lower part, and the greater will overcome the smaller part since it is greater than the other, and the cylinder will roll. But if we imagine on the other side of the intersecting plane that is at right angles to the horizon that there is taken away from the greater part as much as its excess over the smaller part, then the two parts will be in equilibrium, and the whole burden will be at rest on the line that touches the ground, and it will not incline to either side, I mean neither upwards nor downwards. So we need a power equivalent to this to withstand it, and if a small increase is added to this power, it will overcome the burden."

In the last passage there are rather too many pronouns, but the sense is clear: we need a power equal to the excess of the heavy side over the light side to keep the cylinder in place; if we add to the power, we can lift the burden.

No figure is found in the MSS; fig. 13 is a diagram to show what Heron means. The two segments balance each other, and the crescent is the weight with which we have to deal. Heron has seem rightly that the burden must depend on the steepness of the slope, but he has failed to find the right formula, that the pull is proportional to the sine of the angle.

Ch. 24–34 are excerpts from three lost works of Archimedes, on the centre of gravity, on the balance, and on the distribution of weight of a wall placed on columns or a piece of timber carried by a gang of workers. These chapters will be discussed in another paper.

Ch. 34 ends:

> "For the first exposition of the science of mechanics this is enough. In the following we are going to treat of the five powers by which the burdens are moved, and we shall explain their principle and their natural function, and we shall treat of other matters that are of great use in the handling and lifting of burdens.
>
> Here ends the first book of the treatise by Heron on the lifting of heavy things."

From this first Book, the Introduction, it should be possible to form some idea of the sort of person for whom the whole work is written. In ch. 24 Heron writes that it seems to him to be quite necessary to teach "the student of the science of mechanics" something about gravity and centres of gravity.

But this student of the science of mechanics must evidently be well founded in mathematics, if he can follow the solution of the Delian problem in ch. 11, and the theory of the "Taus" in the last paragraph of ch. 18.

His work will evidently be done partly on "paper", such as copying drawings or figures in the same or a different scale, as in ch. 9–19, or constructing a toothed wheel to fit a given screw, as in ch. 19, ult. But when it comes to computing the distribution of weights on columns, it does not only concern a wall on a row of pillars, but also a balk that is to be carried by a crew of workers. It would seem that the student of the science of mechanics is at once the man who designs the building, the engineer who understands the working of the engines, and the overseer who directs the work. In short: an architect, ἀρχιτέκτων, "chief-artificer, master-builder, director of works" according to Liddell and Scott. This impression is strengthened by a study of the two following books.

Book 2

The second Book treats of the five powers, that is the five simple engines: the windlass, the lever, the tackle-block, the wedge, and the screw. First comes a description of each of the powers and their use (ch. 1–6); next the theory of the function of each engine (ch. 7–19); and then the general theory of their function with theoretical examples of their combination (ch. 20–32). Ch. 33–34 relate to the Mechanical Problems of Aristoteles. This work is not mentioned, but a solution is given of several of his problems; we must assume that the other chapters are answers to other collections of problems in this field.

The rest of the Book, ch. 35–41, consists of instructions on how to find the centre of gravity in plane figures of different shapes: a triangle, a quadrangle, and a pentagon or other polygon, and to compute the distribution of its weight if known weights are suspended from its angles.

> "In the name of God the Merciful, the Compassionate
> The second Book of the Treatise by Heron
> on the lifting of heavy things

⟨1⟩ Since the powers by which a given burden is moved by a given power are five, we must of necessity present their form and their theory and their names, because these powers are all related to the same natural principle, though they are very different in form; and as for their names they are as follows: the axle going through a wheel (the windlass), the lever, the pulley, the wedge, the screw.

As for the axle that is fastened to a wheel it is made in this way: a piece of wood, hard and square, like a beam, is procured, its ends are smoothed and turned, and rings of copper are fastened to them, so arranged, that there is no roughness in the axle, in order that it may be so that, if it is fitted into round holes clad with copper in a solid support that does not move, it will turn easily. And this beam, if it is made like this, is called an axle. Then we place on the middle of the axle a wheel pierced by a square hole of the size of the middle of the axle, fitted to the size of the axle, so that it may be so that if the wheel is fitted on the axle, the wheel turns and the axle also, and this wheel is called *bari-ṭrakîn* (*peritrochion*, περιτρόχιον) which means that which surrounds. When we have done this, we cut out in the axle, on either side of the wheel, a shallow, concave groove, so that this furrow can be a winch on which the rope is wound." See fig. 14.

"A shallow groove." Two of the MS have ڢفطس which Carra de Vaux translates "rabotée", while admitting that the word does not exist. One MS reads نقطتين, which is senseless. Nix prints in the text متشكعلا, which would seem to be a conjecture, since the word is not

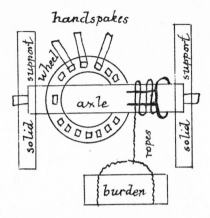

Fig. 14. The illustration for 2:1.
The figure is drawn from the Leiden MS p. 28. In spite of its utter lack of perspective
it is eminently clear. The square holes for the handspakes are cut in the felloe.
The whole drawing is made so that it can be reproduced with ruler and compasses.
The heavy lines on the right hand side of the axle are obviously an afterthought by
some one who has understood from the text that the axle has to be reduced where
the rope comes round it. See text p. 50 sqq.

in the fourth MS; but the critical apparatus here is not quite in order.
Nix translates "eine lockenartige Nute", but the word means "tangled",
"matted", which gives no sense here.

Pappos gives us the Greek text for this chapter, p. 1116, but he has
left out this passage. Later on, where the use of the engine is described,
he has: τὰ... ὅπλα περιθέντες περὶ τὰ σεσιμωμένα τοῦ ἄξονος, which
W. Schmidt translates "so legen wir die Seile ... um die abgehobelten
(und abgerundeten) Teile der Achse ..." The Arabic text here has just
"the grooved part of the axle" without the adjective. But σεσιμωμένος
does not mean "planed", it means "made σιμός", and this word means
1) snub-nosed. From this are derived 2) bent upwards, 3) hollow, concave, 4) rounded and tapered (of a bandage). Heron, as quoted by
Pappos, p. 1130, uses the word about the "tortoises" or sleds: ἡ δὲ
χελώνη πῆγμά ἐστιν ἐκ τετραγώνων ξύλων συμπεπηγός, ὧν τὰ ἄκρα
ἀνασεσίμωται. "The tortoise is put together of square pieces of wood,
whose ends are "up-snub-nosed"", that is, curved softly upwards. The
Arabic text has "whose ends are furrowed", which gives no sense and
shows that Qusṭâ ibn Lûqâ has not quite understood the Greek word.

The conception is that of a soft curve, and that is what we need for the winch, if it is to work in the way described later on. Heron goes on:

> "And we cut out in the surface of the wheel, I mean on its felloe, so many holes as are needed, and they should be made so that if handspakes are fitted into them the wheel and the axle are turned by these handspakes.
>
> We have now made clear how the axle is to be constructed; so now we shall describe its use. If you want to move a great burden by a smaller power, you fasten the ropes that are tied to the burden on the grooved places of the axle on both sides of the wheel. Then you put handspakes into the holes that we have made in the wheel and press down on the handspakes, so that the wheel is turned, and then the burden will be moved by a small power; and the ropes are wound round the axle, or we place them upon each other, so that the whole is not wound up on the axle."

The winch can be used in two ways: for a short haul, say in a crane, the rope is fastened to the drum and wound round it; it must then be rewound before the winch can be used again. For a long haul, several turns of the rope are taken round the drum, and a worker has to keep the rope taut during the winding and coil up the rope on the ground. When the burden has been lifted, the rope can be taken off the drum and lowered for a new burden, without the drum having to be turned at all. For this it is necessary that the place where the rope is wound up should be hollow, so that the coils are always slipping towards the middle.

> "And the size of the engine must be according to the size of the bodies that are to be transported by it. And as for its arrangement, it must be according to the proportion of the burden that we want to move to the power that moves it; that is what we are going to explain later on".
>
> "⟨2⟩ The second power. As for the second power it is the one that is called the lever" (*muḥl*, μοχλός) "and perhaps this power is the first that was considered for the moving of very heavy bodies; because when people wanted to move a very heavy body, since the first thing they needed in moving it was to lift it from the ground, and there was no handle by which to handle it, because all the parts of its bottom were on the ground, they had to find some way for this, and so they dug a small hole in the ground under the heavy body and took a long pole and put its end into the hole and pressed down the other end, and the burden came up (or "became small"). Then they placed under this pole a stone which is called *ibûmaḥliûn*" (*hypomochlion*, ὑπομόχλιον) "and that means that which is placed under the lever, and they pressed down again and the burden became much lighter (or "was lifted higher up"). And as the power became known, it was understood that it was possible to move in this way great burdens. And this pole is called lever" (*muḥl*, μοχλός) "whether it is round or square; and the nearer the stone that is placed under it is to the burden that is to be moved, the easier it becomes to move it, as we are going to explain in the following". See fig. 15.

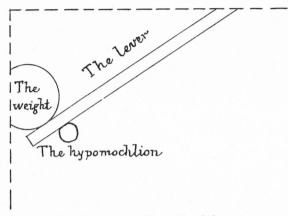

Fig. 15. The lever, illustrating 2:2.
The figure is taken from the Leiden MS, where it is squeezed in on the upper left-hand corner of a verso page, as indicated by the dotted lines. See the text p. 52 sq.

This is a chapter that is found also in Pappos. A translation of his text will show certain discrepancies; but whether this means that Pappos has abbreviated Heron, or that the translator has found it too difficult to follow the Greek text, is not easy to decide. But we must own that Qusṭâ ibn Lûqâ has made a brave struggle. I have followed as far as possible the grammatical construction of the Greek text. Pappos says, p. 1118:

> "The second power was that by means of the lever and was perhaps the first experience of moving exceedingly heavy weights. For people, wanting to move great weights, since these had first to be lifted from the ground, but had no handholds because all the parts of the base of the burden rested on the ground, digging a little way under it and inserting the end of a long pole under the burden, pressed down on the other end, placing under the pole near the burden itself a stone, which is naturally called *hypomochlion*. As the movement proved for them to be quite easy, they understood that is was possible to move great weights in this way. The pole is called lever (*mochlos*) whether it is square or round. The closer the *hypomochlion* is placed to the burden, the easier the weight will be moved, as it will be explained later."

Heron goes on:

> "⟨3⟩ The third power. As for the third power, it is the one that is called the many for lifting (*polyspaston*, πολύσπαστον). If we want to move any weight whatever, we tie a rope to this weight and we want to pull the rope until we lift it, and for this is needed a power equal to the weight that we want to lift. But if we

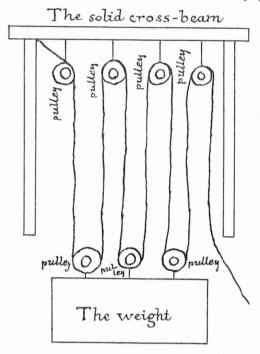

The solid cross-beam

The weight

Fig. 16. The compound pulley, illustrating 2:3.
The figure is taken from the Leiden MS. The first pulley from the left on the cross-beam is quite superfluous. See text p. 53 sqq.

untie the rope from the weight and tie one of its ends to a solid cross-beam and pass its other end over a pulley fastened to the middle of the burden and draw on the rope, our moving of that weight will be easier. And if we fasten on the solid cross-beam another pulley and pass the end of the rope over that and pull it, our moving of that weight will be more easy still. And also if we fasten on this weight another pulley and pass the end of the cord over it, this will augment our ease in moving the weight. And in this way, each time we add pulleys to the solid cross-beam and to the weight we want to lift and pass one end of the rope over the pulley that is on the solid cross-beam and over the pulley that is fastened to the burden and let the ropes that are pulled go from one to the other, we add to the ease of the lifting of the weight. And every time the number of pulleys through which the rope runs is increased, it will be easier to lift that weight. And one end of the rope must be securely tied to the solid cross-beam, and the rope must go from there to the weight. As for the pulleys that are on the solid cross-beam they must be fastened to another piece of wood, turning on a single axle, and this axle is called *manganum* (*manganon*, μάγγανον); and this axle is tied to the solid cross-beam with another rope. And as for the pulleys that are fastened to the burden, they are on another axle like that axle, tied to the burden. And the pulleys must be fitted on the axle in such a way that they cannot touch each other, for if they touch, their turning is difficult. And why we add to the ease of lifting when we add to the number of the pulleys, and why the end of the rope is tied to the solid cross-beam, that we shall explain in the following." See fig. 16.

This chapter is found also in Pappos, with a small lacuna. The only important difference between the two texts is that Qusṭâ ibn Lûqâ has misunderstood the Greek word *kôlon*, κῶλον, "a member", and takes it to mean the pulleys. Pappos says p. 1120:

"The more parts (κῶλα) the rope is bent into, the easier the weight will be lifted" and "the pulleys should be so arranged on the axles, that the parts (κῶλα) do not get entangled and unmanageable (literally: disobedient)".

In both texts we find that if we tie the rope to a fixed point, pass it round a pulley fixed on the burden, and pull, the burden is easier to lift. This is correct, the power needed is reduced by one half. And if we pass the rope over another pulley fixed on the cross-beam, the lifting will be easier still. This is incorrect in so far as the power needed to pull down on the rope is the same as what was needed to pull upwards before the second pulley was used; in practice, however, it is more convenient to pull down than to draw up. The correct theory is given in ch. 11–13.

"⟨4⟩ The fourth power. The fourth power, which comes after this, is the one that is called the wedge (ʾisfîn, σφήν, *sphên*). And this is used for some machines for perfume and for the joining of great works of carpentry, and it has many uses; and its greatest use is when we want to split the bottom of the stone which we want to cut and we have cut its sides free from the mountain from which we cut it. And in this sort of work the rest of the powers cannot do anything, even if we combine them all. But as for the wedge, it will do it by itself alone. And its effect is through blows that strike it, however these blows are, and its effect does not end when the blow stops, and this is evident to us, that without its being struck often there will be noise and splitting of that which its power is bursting apart. And the smaller is the angle of the wedge, the easier is its working, as we shall explain."

Here is the text from Pappos p. 1122:

"The next power is the one through the wedge, and that is of great service in presses for perfumery and the very great joints in carpentry; but greatest of all when it comes to detaching the stones from the quarries from their attachment on the underside; none of all the other powers can do this, not even if they are all joined together, but the wedge does it alone, by any sort of blow, and it does not stop at all because of the workers' pauses, but the increase in force is strong.

This is clear from the fact that even when the wedge is not being struck sometimes noises and cleavings take place through the working of the wedge. The lesser the angle of the wedge becomes, the easier does it work, that is through a smaller blow, as we shall show."

The press for perfumery consisted of a solid, upright frame in which square beams could slide up and down. The mass to be pressed was placed under the lowest beam, and wedges were put in between the beams above. When the wedges were hammered home, a very strong pressure was obtained. A wall painting in Pompeji shows such a press in action (79).

The next point is rather doubtful. Pappos has: πρός . . . τὰς διὰ τῆς τεκτονικῆς ὑπεραγούσας κολλήσεις, "for the very great joints (or: glueings) in carpentry." where κόλλησις may mean either "glueing" or "joint". The first sense is more usual, but I prefer the second one here. At Heron's time the screw-clamp was unknown, so wedges were probably used for most glueings; why then speak of wedges for "very great glueings"? On the other hand, in carpentry, wedges are used for joining floor joists and roof beams, that is, for very great joints.

If we turn to the Arabic text, we find that Carra de Vaux reads وفى لزق

ما حلّ من أعمال النجارة translating: "et pour produire l'adhésion des parties disjointes dans certains ouvrages de menuserie." Nix follows this translation: "und um getrennte Teile von Zimmermannsarbeiten zusammenzufügen." But his text reads:.... وفى الصاق ما جلّ من where الصاق is the reading of the MS B, against لزق in LCK. This means "and in joining of that which is great in works of carpentry", which comes much nearer to the sense of the Greek text; only Qusṭâ ibn Lûqâ has referred the participle "very great" to the works, not to the joints (or glueings). He may even have read ὑπεραγούσης. But the MSS L and B have very clearly حلّ, not جلّ, and the critical apparatus in Nix's edition has nothing about this. What then is جلّ? A printer's error? But it gives a better translation of the Greek text than حلّ. But how then about Nix's translation? The rather disheartening result of a study of this place seems to be that the Teubner edition is not always to be trusted.

⟨5⟩ "The fifth power, and that is the one that is called the screw. As for the engines that we have described, their principles are evident and sufficient in themselves, and this is evident to us in many things in their uses. But as for the screw, in its theory and its use there is a difficulty, whether it is used alone or another power is used together with it. But really the screw is nothing but a twisted

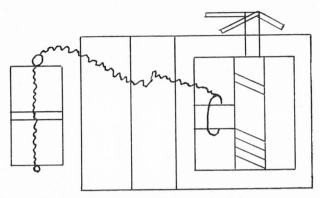

Fig. 17a. The illustration for 2:5.

The figure is taken from the Leiden MS and shows the screw with the *ṭûlus*. To save space, the burden is shown to the left of the engine; since the curly line represents a rope, there is no need to let the burden hang down into the text below. See text p. 56sqq.

wedge which is not hit by blows, but moved by means of a lever, and this will be clear from what we are telling. And we say that the nature of the line that is drawn on it is this: if we imagine one of the sides of a cylindrical shape moving along the surface of the cylinder, and if we imagine a point on the end of this line moving along the side and passing along the whole of it during the time it takes the line to make one turn round the cylindrical shape and to return to the place from which its movement began, then the line that is described by this point on the surface of the cylindrical shape will be one turn of a screw, and this is what is called a screw. If we want to draw this line on the surface of the cylinder, we do it in this way: when we have drawn on some surface two lines, one of which is standing on the other at right angles, one of the lines being equal to the side of the cylinder and the other equal to the circumference of the cylinder, I mean the circumference of its base, and we join the ends of the lines ⟨that enclose⟩ the right angle by a line forming a hypotenuse of the right angle, and we place the line that is equal to the side of the cylinder along the side of the cylinder and the line that is equal to the circumference of the base of the cylinder along the circumference of the base of the cylinder, then the line that is the hypotenuse of the right angle is wound round the surface of the cylinder, and it becomes a screw turn on it. And we can also divide the side of the cylinder in as many equal parts as we want and draw a screw-turn on every one of these parts, and so there will be many turns of the screw on the cylinder, and the cylinder becomes a screw; and the cylinder round which there is laid one hypotenuse is called a screw with one line, I mean when the side of the cylinder is not contained by more than one line, and it begins at one of its ends and goes on to the other. And if we wish to use the screw, we cut out along this line that runs round the cylinder a deep furrow which goes into the substance of the cylinder, so that we can fit into this furrow the piece of wood that is called *ṭûlus* (τύλος, a peg

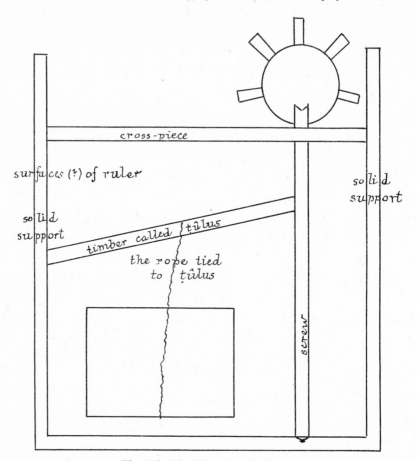

Fig. 17b. The illustration for 2:5.
This figure is taken from the MS B and shows, like fig. 17a, the screw and the *ṭūlus*. The subject is the same in the two figures, but the treatment is quite different. The lettering is very slovenly, in a hand quite different from that of the text. See text p. 56 sqq.

or knob). Then we use the screw in this wise: we turn smooth its two ends and fit them into holes drilled in solid supports, so that their turning in these holes is easy. And we arrange the piece of wood called ruler (*qânûn*, κάνων), upright parallel to the wooden screw. And there should be in this ruler a deep furrow like a canal, in that side of the ruler that faces the screw. Then we fit one end of the piece of wood that is called *ṭūlus* into the screw furrow and the other end into the furrow in the ruler. And when we wish to lift a heavy burden with this engine, we take a rope among the ropes called weapon (ὅπλον, tool, gear, rope, weapon) and make fast one of its ends to the burden we want to lift, and the other to the piece of wood called *ṭûlus*. And we have already drilled in the end of the screw holes opposite one another, so now we put handspakes into the holes and turn the screw with these handspakes, and then the *ṭûlus* is lifted because it engages the furrow that is in the screw, and by its lifting the rope is lifted and the weight that is tied to it is raised. We can also in stead of the handspakes fit a square with handles on the end of the screw that projects beyond the solid support, and we turn the screw by means of this square, and the burden is lifted. And as for the screw furrow that is on the cylinder, it is sometimes square and sometimes lentilshaped. And the square one, that is the rectangular furrow whose furrow ends in two lines, and the lentilshaped one is the one where the furrow is sloping and ends in a single line. And this is called lentilshaped, and the other is called square."

See fig. 17a and b.

The text in Pappos is very nearly the same. In stead of "a square with handles" he writes p. 1126: "It is possible in stead of the handspakes to put a handle round the end of the screw projecting outside the frame and thus to lift the burden by turning the handle." Here is nothing about the square mentioned in the Arabic text. Probably Pappos has abridged Heron. The square is discussed in the next chapter.

Qusṭâ ibn Lûqâ has had trouble with the Greek text, since he has only one Arabic word, screw, with which to translate two Greek words: ἕλιξ, spiral, and κοχλίας, snail. So he makes ἕλιξ, which is used only thrice, "screw turn", reserving "screw" alone for κοχλίας, which is the common expression. The words τύλος and κάνων he has taken over, but ὅπλον he translates once into "weapon", but does not use this word any more. The repetition of the names of the screw-thread: square and lentilshaped, is explained by the Greek text having two words: φακοειδής, which is just a description, and φακωτός, which is the technical name for the lentil-shaped screw-thread. In the Arabic text the same word is used twice.

Both Hultsch, the editor of Pappos, and Nix take the furrow in the "ruler" to be undercut. The Greek word σωλήν means just a gutter, if it does not mean a pipe. The same word is used for the furrow in the screw; and if Heron here wanted an undercut furrow, I should expect him to be more explicit. The Greek text has: κανόνα... σωλῆνα ἔχοντα μέσον ἐν τῇ ἄνω ἐπιφανείᾳ where Hultsch suggests ἐναντίον for ἄνω. The Arabic version: "in that side of the ruler that faces the screw" supports Hultsch's conjecture.

"⟨6⟩ When the screw is used by itself alone, it is used in this way. And when it is used in another way, in combination with another power, and that is what

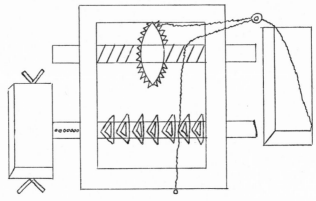

Fig. 18a. The illustration for 2:6. The figure, which shows the screw and the cog-
wheel, is taken from the MS L. (3:4). See the text p. 59 sqq.

is done with the axle on which there is fitted a wheel, then it is done in this way.
Let us imagine that the wheel which is on the axle has teeth and a screw that
fits the wheel is placed either at right angles to the ground or parallel to the surface of the ground, and let the teeth be engaged in the screw furrow, and the ends
of the screw are in holes bored in solid supports as we have already described.
And let there be on one end of the screw sticking out beyond the solid support
an extension on which there is fitted a square with handles, or we bore through
this projecting extension holes in which we can fit handspakes with which to
turn the screw. And if we wish to lift some weight with this engine, we make fast
the ropes that are tied to the burden on the axle on both sides of the wheel, and
we turn the screw, with which we have engaged the teeth of the wheel, and so
the wheel turns, and the axle, and that burden is raised."

See fig. 18a and 18b.

The Greek text in Pappos (p. 1128) is very similar, the only difference
being once more that he does not speak of any square: "... either some
handle may be round (the projecting end of the screw) by which the
screw is turned, or ..." The Greek text calls the wheel "toothed",
ὠδοντωμένον; the Arabic text here uses the word رَتَّك which is generally the translation of σκυτάλη, hand-spake. For the use of this word
in Greek to design the teeth of a wheel see p. 202.

Figure 18a, from MS L, is somewhat less clear than most of the others.
We find one axle with a cog-wheel, the latter shown foreshortened as a pri-
mitive ellipse formed by two arcs. There is a screw, which is here made up
of a row of double triangles. The axle of the screw projecting on the
left has first a row of holes, next a big square head with a pair of very

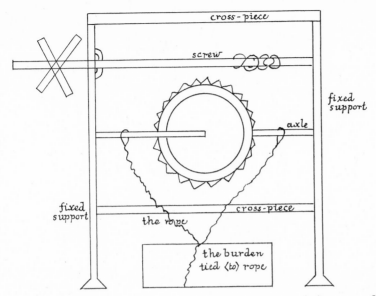

Fig. 18b. The illustration for 2:6, taken from the MS B. (3:4). See text p. 59 sqq.

small hand-spakes projecting from either end. A better shape is shown in fig. 52a. The burden is placed to the right of the frame, but the rope from it ends in a ring, from which one rope seems to reach the cog-wheel, another rope the frame. The oblique lines on the axle for the cog-wheel must be meant for the windings of the rope, but they have no connexion with the ropes shown. The two axles should be at right angles. Since the draughtsman could not foreshorten the screw, he has foreshortened the wheel just to indicate that the two axles are not parallel. For other ways of drawing a screw see figs. 9a,b, 17a,b, 18b, 28a,b.

Fig. 18b, from MS B, is very clear indeed.

"⟨7⟩ As for the construction of the five powers that we have just described, and their use, we have said and explained enough about them. But the reason why each of those engines is able to move the great weights by a small power, that is what we are going to tell now in this way." (See fig. 19). "Let us imagine two circles round the same centre, and that is the point A, and let their diameters be BĞ and DH, and let the circles turn about the point A, which is their centre. And let the circles be at right angles to the horizon, and let us hang on the two points B, Ğ, two equal weights, and they are Z, Ḥ. Then it is evident to us that the circles do not decline to any side whatever, because the two weights Z, Ḥ,

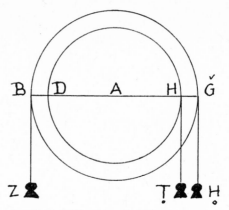

Fig. 19. The illustration for 2:7. The figure is taken from the MS L; it is not found
in the MS B. See text p. 61 sq.

are equal and the two distances BA, AǦ, are equal, and BǦ is a balance-beam turning on a point of suspension, which is the point A. And if we move the weight which
is at Ǧ and hang it on H, ⟨and that is the sign Ṭ,⟩ the weight Z will decline downwards to that which is below, and the circles will move; but if we add to the weight
Ṭ, it will balance the weight Z, and the ratio of the weight Ṭ to the weight Z
will be as the ratio of the distance BA to the distance AH. And we consider the
line BH as a balance turning on a point of suspension, which is the point A, and this
Archimedes has explained in his book on the equalizing of declination (on equilibrium, περὶ ἰσορροπιῶν). And from this it is evident that it is possible to move a
great bulk by a small power, because when the two circles are on the same centre
and the great weight is on an arc from the small circle and the small power is on
an arc from the great circle, and the ratio of the line from the centre of the big
one to the line from the centre of the small one is greater than the ratio of the
great weight to the small power that moves it, then the small power will prevail
against the great weight."

The addition "and that is the sign Ṭ" is not necessary for under-
standing the text, but seems to me necessary for reasons of style. The
proof that a small power will lift a great burden is a development of
Book 1, ch. 34, where it is shown by a somewhat similar figure that any
small weight will balance a given great weight. That chapter is probably
taken from a lost work of Archimedes On Balances, περὶ ζυγῶν.

"Decline" is the Arabic version of ῥέπειν, which means of a balance
that it deviates from the horizontal position. The Arabic word for
equilibrium has nothing to do with this word; so Qusṭâ ibn Lûqâ translates ἰσορροπία by "equalizing declination".

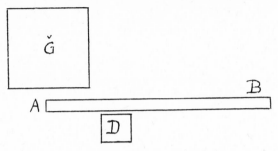

Fig. 20. The lever, illustrating 2:8.
The figure is taken from the Leiden MS; it shows the lever in a horizontal position,
carrying the whole weight of the burden. See text p. 63 sq.

The quotation from Archimedes is from his On the Equilibrium of
Plane Figures, Book 1, ch. 6–7.

"⟨8⟩ Since we have found that this is true by our example with the circles,
we now wish to prove this on these five powers, and we have given the proof,
when this is done. The ancient authors, who came before us, have also started
from this starting-point. Now let us first prove this on the tool that is called the
lever. Now, this lever moves heavy things in two ways: either by being placed
in a position that is parallel to the ground, or by being lifted from the ground,
sloping towards it. And its use consists in that its end that is lifted from the
ground is pressed towards the ground. Let us first imagine it parallel to the
ground," (See fig. 20) "and let the lever be the line AB, and let the weight that
is moved by the lever be on the point A, and that is the weight Ǧ, and let the
moving power be at the point B, and let the stone that is under the lever on
which the lever turns be at the point D, and let BD be greater than the line DA.
If we then raise the end of the lever which is the sign B and lift the lever from
the stone on which it turns, then the weight which is Ǧ will be moved to the opposite side, and the point B will describe a circle round the centre D, and the point
A will also describe a circle round that centre, smaller than the circle which the
point B describes. And if the ratio of the line BD to the line DA is the same
as the ratio of the weight which is Ǧ to the power which is at B, then the weight
Ǧ will balance the power B. But if the ratio of BD to DA is greater than the
ratio of the weight to the power, then the power will prevail over the weight,
because the two circles are on the same centre, and the weight is on the arc of
the small circle and the moving power is on the arc of the large circle; and so
it is evident to us that there happens to the lever that which happened to the
two circles on the same centre, and so the reason of the lever that moves the
burden is the same as the reason that belongs to the two circles."

Among the ancient authors we can reckon Aristoteles, whose Mechanical Problems always are solved by a reference to concentric circles.
The lever is discussed in his Problem 3.

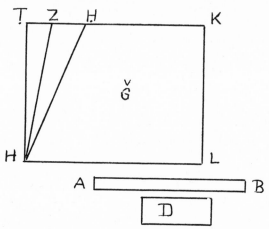

Fig. 21 a, the illustration for 2:9. The figure is taken from the MS L and shows a lever lifting one edge of a burden. Cf. figs 20b, c, and text p. 64 sqq.

To say that we lift the lever from the stone is not correct; as long as the burden can move downwards, the lever must stay in contact with the fulcrum. What is meant is that we move the lever in the direction away from the stone.

This is the first of the two ways of using the lever: the lever is horizontal and carries the whole weight of the burden. The other way: when the lever is more or less upright and is inserted under one edge of a burden resting on the ground, is discussed in the next chapter. See fig. 21 a and b.

"⟨9⟩ And let us also imagine a lever, which is the line AB, turning about a stone under the lever, and that is D, and let one of the ends of the lever, the one which is the point A, be under the burden Ğ, and let the other end be lifted from the ground, and that is by the point B. If we now press down the end of the lever which is by the point B towards the ground, we will move the weight Ğ. And I contend that it is not moved by this procedure in the same way as it was moved by the other procedure, because by this procedure part of the weight is moved and part of it remains resting on the ground. Let us now imagine a surface going from the point H at right angles to the horizon, and let the excess of the weight be HZŢ, and let this weight which is HZŢ be in equilibrium with the weight which is HZH, and if we imagine this weight which is the whole of HHŢ cut off from the burden lying on the place on which it is, then it will not decline to any side whatever, neither towards the side Ţ nor towards the side H, because the two weights HŢZ, HHZ are at equilibrium with one another. And so the part of the burden which is HHŢ will not need any power at all. And so the part

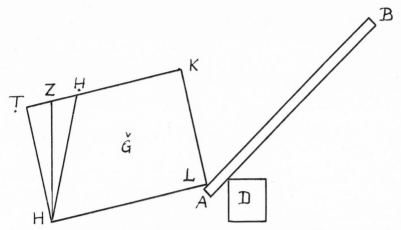

Fig. 21b. My reconstruction of fig. 21a. See text p. 64 sqq.

of the burden that is HHKL is the one that the lever moves; and if the lever AB
was moving the whole of the weight HTKL, then the ratio BD to DA would
be as the ratio of the weight HTKL to the power that is at B; it does not, however, move the whole of it, and that is because the imagined surface holds part
of it, and that is one half; because this surface, if we do not imagine it and we
increase the moving power by a measure corresponding to this excess, the power
would be pressed downwards and the end of the lever that is at A will go upwards,
because the weights will be divided towards the power that moves them by a
balanced division, and so the imagined surface takes off half of the burden. And
so if the power that is at B balances the weight HHKL, the ratio of BD to DA
is like the ratio of the weight HHKL to the power B, and the measure which
raises the burden from the ground, in this measure is needed less of the power;
and it is placed in a position that does not need any power, if the imagined surface
going through the sign H at right angles to the horizon divides the burden into
two halves. And this effect of the lever can be referred to the circle, but it is
not the same as the first effect.

And that the balance also can be referred to the circle is evident, because
the circle is a sort of balance."

Part of this chapter is incomprehensible and seems to me to be
corrupt. Here is Carra de Vaux's translation; see fig. 21 c.

"... mais il ne le meut pas tout entier, car une partie en est adhérente au
plan supposé, et cette partie est la moitié du poids total[2] ([2] *La moitié*. C'est un
rapport pris pour exemple.); si, en effet, nous n'imaginions pas ce plan et que
nous ajoutions à la puissance motrice une quantité correspondant à la portion
du poids qu'il tient en èquilibre, l'extrémité du levier où agit la puissance serait
repoussée vers le bas, et le bout α s'élèverait, parce que les puissances agissent

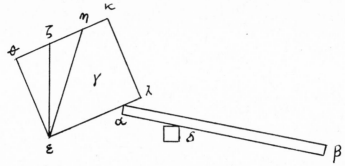

Fig. 21c. The figure of the lever given by Carra de Vaux and Nix. See p. 65 sq. where their texts are quoted.

sur les poids selon la loi de proportionnalité. Le plan supposé retient donc la moitié du poids; alors, si la puissance appliquée en β fait équilibre au poids εηκλ, le rapport $\dfrac{\beta\delta}{\delta\alpha}$ sera égal au rapport du poids εηκλ à la force β; et la quantité de puissance nécessaire pour élever le poids à partir du sol sera moindre que précédemment[1] ([1] *Que précédemment*. Nous ajoutons ces mots.)."

And here is the translation by Nix:

"... er bewegt sie aber nicht ganz, weil ein Teil der Last durch die angenommene (senkrechte) Ebene gehalten wird, und dieser Teil sei z.B. die Hälfte. Denken wir uns nämlich jene (senkrechte) Ebene nicht, [so dass das Ganze als Wage um den Punkt δ erscheint,] und fügen der bewegenden Kraft einen jenem Überschuss (der als Beispiel vorgenannten Hälfte der Last) gleichen Betrag hinzu, so wird die Kraft nach unten gedrückt, und das Hebelende bei α hebt sich, weil die Lasten sich auf die bewegenden Kräfte gleichmässig, (nicht proportional, wodurch Gleichgewichtslage einträte) verteilen. Also nimmt die gedachte Ebene die Hälfte der Last weg. Wenn nun die Kraft bei β der Last εηκλ das Gleichgewicht hält, so verhält sich also βδ zu δα wie die Last εηκλ zur Kraft β; und es bedarf einer um so viel geringeren Kraft, als sich die Last von der Erde hebt."

Nix has put into parentheses his own comments; the sentence which I have put into brackets is not in the text.

I cannot see that either of the two editors has made any real sense out of the passage. Both have supposed that the sentence "and that is one half" means "and let us assume that this part is one half", but without any warrant in the text. But apart from this the whole calculation is wrong. If a burden is resting on the ground and we lift one edge, while the other edge is still on the ground, we lift only half of its weight. As we lift, it will turn on the edge that is at rest, and the weight of the burden to be lifted by the lever will be reduced by twice the weight of the part that lies outside a vertical plane through this edge. When the vertical plane divides the burden into two halves, it will be in equilibrium.

I have no doubt that this is what Heron said, and it is clear that the text does not say it. But we find most of the necessary elements: that only one edge of the burden is lifted; that twice the weight of the overhang has to be disregarded; that the burden grows lighter, the more it is lifted; and that it will reach a point where it is in equilibrium. On the strength of this I venture to regard the remark about "half the weight", which gives no real sense where it stands, as a remnant of the correct explanation of the working of the lever in this position; but I cannot see any way to produce a likely text.

The figure is very poor; it ought to be turned so that the line HZ becomes vertical, but even then it is not good. I think that it has taken up this position to save space. I have added my own interpretation, fig. 21 b; and also that of Carra de Vaux, which is repeated by Nix, to illustrate the two translations quoted, fig. 21 c.

> "⟨10⟩ And as for the axle that goes through the wheel, it is nothing else but two circles on the same axle, one of them small, and that is the circle of the axle, and the other big, and that is the circle of the wheel. And so it is correct that the hanging of the weight is from the axle, and the moving power is on the wheel, because by this arrangement the small power prevails over the great burden. And this is what those before us have already told; we have explained it here, however, just to make our book complete and to give it an orderly composition."

Nix in the last passage has corrected وصفناها into وضعناها trans- lating "wir haben ihn [den Sats] hierhergesetzt"; but it seems to me unnecessary. Carra de Vaux follows the text and translates "nous ne l'avons répété que pour que notre livre soit complet". The sense is the same anyway.

The theory of the winch is given by Aristoteles in Problem 13, see p. 14.

> "⟨11⟩ And let us now speak of the reason for the engine that is called the many for lifting (the compound pulley, πολύσπαστον)." (See fig. 22 a and b.) "Let us imagine a pulley hung at the point A and on it a "weapon" rope, and that is BǦ, and we make fast on the two taut ends of the cord a weight, and that is D; and let this weight be hanging above the ground. Then it is evident that the two taut parts of the rope will be stretched equally, and each of them will carry one half of the weight D, because if the two taut parts were not equal, the one that was higher would pull up the one that was lower down. But we do not see anything like that, for both the taut parts of the rope are at rest. If we now divide

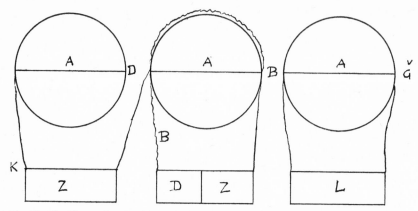

Fig. 22a, the illustration for 2:11. The figure is taken from the MS L (0.85:1); it shows three figures to illustrate the theory of the single pulley, but none of them corresponds to the text. See fig. 21b and text p. 67 sqq.

the weight D into halves, I mean into two equal parts, it is evident to us that the two taut parts of the rope will stay at rest, because the burden that stretches them is the same, to wit the same that stretched them before, and one half of the weight balances the weight that is equal to it. And the two taut parts of the rope will be equal for another reason, to wit that equal burdens are suspended from equal lines, which means that the taut rope touches, on the arc of the pulley, two points opposite one another, and their distances from the centre is the same, and the weights are as if they were suspended from these points.

And by this arrangement and in this way a heavy burden or a great weight does not balance a small power, and that is why this form of the engine that is called the many for lifting is called the one with a single lift; and this one that is called the one with the single lift is the one in which the rope is stretched in two parts."

For the "weapon" rope see p. 58.

That the burden will right itself if it is placed in an oblique position is theoretically correct; it takes for granted that there is no friction and that the rope is without weight, for otherwise the long part of the rope would be heavier than the short part, and so counteract the movement of the burden.

The figure for chapter 11 in the Leiden MS is shown in fig. 22a; it does not correspond to the text. The pulley on the right might illustrate the text, if the letter on the weight had been a D, but it is an unmistakeable L. The other letters do not correspond to the text, and the rope going from the weight KZ to the pulley in the middle is incomprehen-

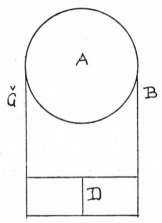

Fig. 22b. My reconstruction of fig. 22a. See text p. 67 sqq.

sible. It looks as if the scribe had confused the figure for ch. 11 with that for ch. 12.

It is easy to construct the figure from the text, as shown in fig. 22b.

"⟨12⟩ And now let us explain that which has two lifts, and that is the one that has three taut parts of the rope, and in this way every time the taut parts of the rope are increased in number and their stretching is repeated, by the number of these repeatings the engine is said to have so many lifts, after one has been substracted from the number of repeatings of the stretchings of the rope, so that the name names the number that is less than that number, I mean: one less than the repeatings of the rope." (See fig. 23) "Let us now imagine an end of the rope which is at D going over a pulley and going from there to a solid support which is by the pulley A by the sign Ḥ, and the taut parts of the rope are equal for the reason that we have explained, because every one of them is stretched by one third of the weight; and if the weight Z is divided into three equal parts, so that that of it which is near the side ṬB is the double of Ǧ, then the weight will be at rest, and will not decline at all towards any side, and the weight that is suspended from the rope Ǧ will balance the weight that is suspended from the rope HL" (so the MSS; Nix reads D) "and that is double that of the other side. Now if we place in stead of Ǧ which is one third of the weight a power that balances the weight, the rope will be held, and the rest of the weight will not prevail over it, although it is smaller that that, and this is so also if we put the end of the rope that is by Ḥ over a pulley which is fastened at Ḥ and stretch it till we can fasten its end to the weight Z at the point K; and every one of the taut ropes carries one fourth of the burden. And if the burden once more is divided by another division, so that that of it which is near the sign ṬBǦ" (so Nix; the MSS have ṬHB) "is three times that which is near the sign K, then the weight that is by the sign K will balance the rest of the weight, and the ratio of the num-

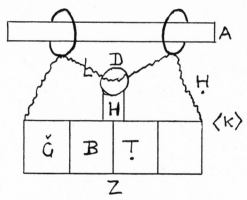

Fig. 23. The illustration for 2:12.
The figure is taken from the Leiden MS and illustrates the explanation of the "double lift" with one pulley on the burden and two on the cross-beam. See text p. 69 sq.

ber of taut ropes that carry the weight to the rope that pulls it will be as the ratio of the weight to the weight. And by all these weights it is necessary that the ratio of the known weight to the power that moves it is as the ratio of the taut ropes that carry the burden to the ropes that the moving power moves. This is an example: if the burden is fifty talents and the moving power is five talents, the taut ropes that carry the weight must be ten times the ropes that the power of five talents pulls on, so that the taut ropes that carry the weight are ten and the rope that is by the moving power is one. And if the ropes that carry the weight are twenty ropes, then the ropes that are by the moving power will be two ropes, and in this way the power balances the weight; and if we want the power to prevail over the weight, we must either increase the power or we must increase the ropes that carry the weight. So we have explained the pulley that is called the many for lifting, and from this it is evident for us, that it is possible to move the known weight by the known power.

On line 3 of p. 125 of the German edition I read بمدة for يمد; it makes no difference in the sense.

The figure for chapter 12, fig. 23, is taken from the Leiden MS. It corresponds to the text, except that the letter K is lacking. Carra de Vaux and Nix have disregarded the letters H and L on the figure, and so have to correct HL to D. The other correction, ṬHB into ṬBǦ is necessary.

It seems to me that the text is incomplete, in so far as I should expect a more full description of the figure; it is taken for granted in a way that is not usual in Heron. But the sense of the chapter is quite plain, and there seems to be no need to try to reconstruct the text.

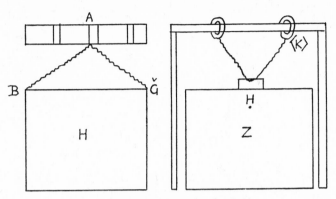

Fig. 24. The illustration for 2:13.
The figure is taken from the Leiden MS (3:4) and shows on the left the "single lift" with the pulley on the cross-beam, on the right the "double lift" with the pulley on the burden. See text p. 71 sq.

"⟨13⟩ But now it happens by some procedure that the double taut rope in two parts only is called sometimes "with one lift" and sometimes "with two lifts" after the measure of power that we use for it. (See fig. 24). And an instance of this is if we imagine a pulley by the sign A and a cord on it, and let the taut parts of the cord be at the two signs BǦ, and let BǦ be fastened to a weight H. If we now divide this weight into two halves, the two parts that are on the two sides will balance one another, and this pulley is called "with one lift", because the power in this balances the weight of the same size. And let us imagine again another weight on the sign Z, and we tie to it a pulley and that is the pulley Ḥ, and we pass over this pulley a rope and tie its two ends to a solid cross-beam, so that weight Z is hanging. Now each of the two taut ends of the cord carry one half of the weight, and if somebody unties the end of the rope tied at K and keeps holding the rope, then he will carry one half of that weight, and the whole of the weight will be twice the power that holds it. And it is evident from this that another power from the solid cross-beam in the end of the taut rope corresponding to the power that holds the other end also draws the weight, and therefore this pulley is called correctly the one with two lifts; and so the double rope divided into two taut parts may be called "with one lift" and "with two lifts"; and from this it is evident to us that the other end must be tied to the solid cross-beam, not to the weight placed for lifting, because the power that comes from this solid support balances the moving power and helps it in moving the weight. And it is evident that if one end of the rope is tied to the burden, then the burden will balance a power equal to itself, but if the other end of it is tied to a solid cross-beam, then the power will balance twice the weight, and the weight will be moved by a power less than the power that was moving it the first time".

The figure for ch. 13, fig. 24, is taken from the Leiden MS; it cor-

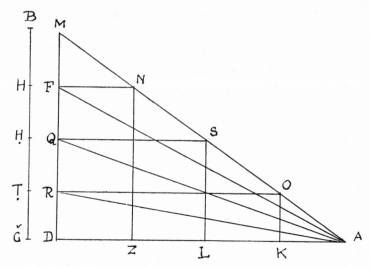

Fig. 25. The illustration for 2:15.
The figure is taken from the MS L; it illustrates the theory of the wedge. See text p. 72 sq.

responds to the text, except that the letter K is lacking. I cannot explain
the vertical lines on the cross-beam A.

> "⟨14⟩ As for the wedge, the blow must move it during a given time, for there
> can be no movement without time, and this blow works by a mere touch, which
> does not stay with the wedge, not even the shortest time. And it is evident to us
> from this that the wedge moves on after the blow has stopped. And we learn
> this also in another way: during a certain time after the blow there comes from
> the wedge noises and splinters from the splitting by its edge. And that the blow,
> though it does not stay on the wedge, not even for the shortest time, has its effect
> on it, that is evident to us from the stones that are flung and the arrows, whether
> they are flung by hand alone or by some other engine, because after the stone
> leaves the hand we see it reach a far away place with power, though the hand
> does not propel it. And from this it is evident to us that the blow does not stay
> on the wedge for even the shortest time, but that the wedge after the blow begins
> to move".

The word "arrow" is probably a translation of βέλος, which means
any sort of missile. The law of inertia was imperfectly understood at
this time, but the analogy between the wedge and the stone flung from
the hand is correct.

> "⟨15⟩ Now I contend that any blow, even if it is slight, will move any wedge.
> (See fig. 25) Let us imagine a wedge whose edge is at the sign A, and let its head

be the line DM. And let the blow that moves it be BǦ, and let its distance" (i.e. the way it has travelled) "be AD. And let it be possible to move by a slight blow, and let us take away from the blow BǦ a blow that is the blow BH, and this is less than all known blows. Then I say that the blow BH by itself will drive in a certain part of the wedge. The proof this is that the blow BǦ moves the distance AD, and HǦ moves a distance less than AD, let it move the distance AZ, and then, if the blow BH is added, the distance will be AD, which is moved by the blow BǦ. And thus the blow BH by itself moves the distance DZ. And if we imagine a blow BǦ divided into blows equal to BH, and they are BH, HḤ, ḤṬ, ṬǦ, and if the distance AD is divided into parts equal to DZ, and they are AK, KL, LZ, ZD, then each of the blows BH, HḤ, ḤṬ, ṬǦ will move each of the distances DZ, ZL, LK, KA. Let us now imagine lines parallel to the line DM, which is the head of the wedge, and these are the lines ZN, LS, KO, and also lines parallel to the line AD, and they are the lines FN, QS, RO, and the lines DR, RQ, QF, FM are equal, and if we join the points FQR with the point A, there will result four wedges, whose edges are at the point A, and their heads are the lines MF, FQ, QR, RD, and each of them is moved by a blow equal to the blow BH a distance equal to the line AD, and it is the same if we say that the blow BH drives the whole wedge the distance DZ, that is the distance KA, and that the blow BH drives the wedge whose head is RD the distance AD, for by the movement of the whole wedge the line KO is moved the distance AK, and by the movement of the wedge whose head is DR it is moved the distance that is equal to the line KO, and that is the distance RD from AD, and so RD moves by the blow BH the distance AD; and from this it is clear to us that the measure of the blow BH to BǦ is the measure of the wedge whose head is RD to the whole of the wedge, and in the same way also it is with the amount of the time in which the wedge whose head is the line RD is moved, and the amount of the movement of the distance which the whole wedge is moved by the blow BǦ; and the ratio of this is again like the ratio of the blow BH to the whole blow. And also from another point of view we do not find any difference between the moving of the head DM, I mean the whole wedge, by the blow BǦ, and the moving by every single blow BH, HḤ, ḤṬ, ṬǦ of every one of the wedges whose heads are MF, FQ, QR, RD, because the partial blows are equal to the whole blow, and the blow BH drives the wedge whose head is MF in the measure in which the whole blow drives the whole wedge, and each of the remaining blows drives each of the remaining wedges. And if that which is driven in is one of the small wedges, if it is hit by many blows and is driven in, then it is driven in as far as the whole wedge is driven in by one whole blow, and this is by a movement corresponding to the blows, I mean by the measure of the blows BH, HḤ, ḤṬ, ṬǦ, and in the same way the ratio of the time to the time is like the ratio of the blow to the blow, and the head of the whole wedge to the head of one of the small wedges; and the smaller is the angle of the wedge, the further will the wedge penetrate by a smaller power than the power that drives in the whole wedge".

"⟨16⟩ After this there remains to explain the theory of the screw. So let us first begin by putting down how it is with the screw turn. And we say that when

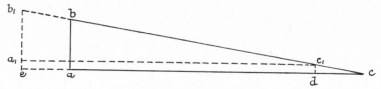

Fig. 26, illustrating 2:16.
This is my own figure, showing Heron's templet for making a screw. The explanation in found in the text p. 74 sq.

we want to make a screw, we take a hard, strong piece of wood, whose length is according to our need; and the part of it where we want to make the screw should be turned, and its thickness should be the same in all its parts, so that its surface is a cylinder; and we mark on its surface a side of the cylinder (a straight line, a generator) and we divide this side into equal parts of the size of the height of the screw turn; and we draw on a surface two straight lines at right angles to one another, and let us make one of the two lines equal to the circumference of the cylinder, and the other of the size of the height of the screw turn; and let us join the ends of the two lines by a line forming the hypotenuse of the right angle. And we make a triangle out of thin brass, equal to this triangle, and it should be so thin that we can bend it any way we wish. And when we have done this we place the side that is equal to the height of the screw turn on the first of the equal divisions into which we have divided the side of the cylinder. Then we fold the thin triangle of brass round the wooden cylinder and let the remaining, acute angle of the triangle reach the right angle of the brass figure, since the base of the triangle is equal to the circumference of the cylinder. Then we fasten the two angles to one another, and we draw the screw turn along the hypotenuse of the right angle. Then we turn the triangle towards the second division, and we place the side of the thin triangle along the second part, and in the same way as before we draw the second turn of the screw in continuation of the first turn, and we do this till we have drawn all the divisions of the wooden cylinder. And because by the use of the screw we have to place in the first furrow that is in the screw turn the piece of wood that is called *ṭûlus*, and this is what lifts the weight, by the turning of the screw it will lift this piece of wood and as it is lifted the weight will be lifted".

The last sentence will give better sense if the word "because" is left out. I suggest that من اجل is a translation of the words περὶ αὐτῷ belonging to the sentence just before: "till we have drawn on all the divisions of the wooden cylinder a line *round it*. In the use of the screw ..."

Heron's method for designing a screw is not only theoretically correct, but also practicable; the only difficulty is in fastening the acute angle of the templet to the right angle, if it is made accurately to measure. It would be better to have a little overlap. In fig. 26 abc is the templet,

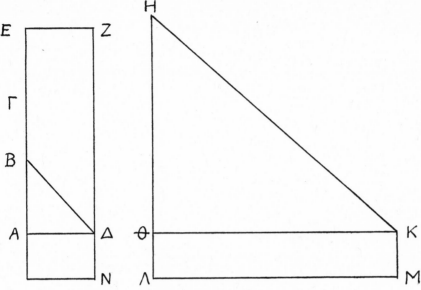

Fig. 27, illustrating 2:16.
The figure is taken from Pappos, from the Vatican MS; it shows the cylinder for the screw, EZN, and the templet, HΛM. The explanation is given in the text p. 75 sq.

where ab is the height of the screw thread, ac the circumference of the cylinder. If we want a lug for soldering, say dcc_1, we have to prolong ca to e, where ae = cd; put up eb_1 parallel to ab, where $eb_1 = dc_1 + ab$, and prolong cb to b_1. We now have $a_1b_1c_1 = abc$, mounted on the square a_1c_1de, with cdc_1 for the joint.

That the templet has developed like this we can see from Pappos p. 1110. See fig. 27.

> "Let there be imagined a cylinder turned to an even thickness, AΔEZ, its side being AE, and let the height of a single screw line on it be supposed to be AB; and let there be made a strip of sheet bronze, of which the part HΘK should be a rectangular triangle with the right angle at Θ, and the rest a rectangle, ΘKΛ; and let HΘ equal AB, and ΘK equal the circumference of the cylinder AΔEZ. Then let the strip be wound round the cylinder, so that the rectangle ΘKΛ will also become a cylinder, fitting ΔE, (or AΔN?) when the latter is put into it, and let Θ come at A, and H at B, and thus let us draw along the twisted hypotenuse HK the socalled single screw line like AB. Then we move the strip again, so that Θ comes at B, and H at Γ, and draw along HK another single screw-line, so that the whole line now has two windings".

After this, the text is corrupt, but the sense is clear: to make a lentil-shaped screw we have to bisect the lines AB, BΓ, &c, and draw a second line like the first one to serve as a guide for the bottom of the thread; then we make the furrow with a file.

In 1936 I made a model of Heron's screw-cutter (18), see p. 139 sq, and followed Pappos rather than Heron; only I made a lug on the templet and soldered it, according to Heron. I found out that the easiest way to move the templet along the wood was to screw it along. So Heron's words "... we turn the triangle ..." go to show that he had practical experience of the method.

Fig. 27 is taken from the Vatican MS (89). The proportions are absurd, since HΘ should equal BA. The letter N is not mentioned in the text, but it is clear that the cylinder AΔN should correspond to the square ΘKΛM, as I have suggested by a tentative conjecture. The line ΔB represents one complete turn of the screw line, from A to B. The following figures will show that such a diagonal line joining two points one whole turn apart is a conventional sign for a screw turn.

"⟨17⟩ Now we must take the screw to be just a twisted wedge, for the triangle from which we draw the screw line is really a wedge, and its head is the side which is equal to the height of the screw turn, and the acute angle of the wedge is the other angle of the triangle by which the piece of wood called *ṭûlus* is found. And so the screw becomes a turned, twisted wedge, which is worked, not by a blow, but by turning, and its turning here replaces the blows on the wedge; and so it lifts the weight, and its lifting of the burden is the opposite of the work done by the wedge, because the wedge works by penetrating deep, and this moves the weight, but the weight stays in its place; but as for the screw, it is a twisted wedge and it stays in its place and lifts the burden towards itself. And just as it has been explained about the wedge that the one that has a smaller angle moves the weight by less power than the power that moves the weight by a wedge with a greater angle, so we have to say about this that the screw in which the distances between the screw lines are less will move the weight with greater ease than the screw whose distances between the screw lines are greater will move it, because the lesser distance gives a smaller angle. And the screw whose windings are steeper will move the weight by means of a greater power, and the one that is softer will move the weight by means of a lesser power".

"⟨18⟩ When it is the case that a wheel with teeth engages the screw furrow, then for every one turn the screw is turned, it will move one tooth of the wheel. And we can prove this in the following way." (See fig. 28a).

"We imagine a screw, which is the screw AB, and let the screw line which is on it be AǦ, DH, ZḤ, and let every one of the screw lines be a single turn. And let us imagine a wheel placed here, provided with teeth, which is ḤǦHṬ, and its teeth are ḤǦ, ǦH, HṬ, and it is engaged with the screw turn, and the

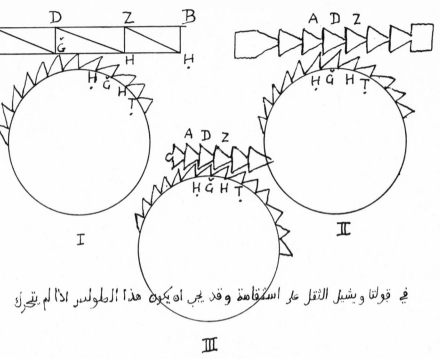

في قولنا ويشيل الثقل على استقامة وقد يجب ان يكون هذا الطولس الا لم يتحرك

Fig. 28a. The illustration for 2:18.
The figure is taken from the Leiden MS; it shows, in three versions, a cog-wheel
engaging a screw. The explanation is given in the text p. 76 sqq.

tooth ǦH is engaged in the screw turn completely, and so the other teeth will
not be engaged in the other screw turns. If we turn the screw until the point H
is moved towards the place Ǧ, H will come where Ǧ is, [and] (*delevi*) when the
screw makes a single turn, and the tooth ǦH comes into the place of the tooth
ǦH, and the tooth HṬ into the place of the tooth ǦH, and the tooth HṬ also
into the place of the tooth ǦH, and so in one turning of the screw the whole
distance between the teeth turns" (i.e. the wheel turns as far as the distance
between any two teeth). "And like this we have to imagine that it will be about
the rest of the teeth And as many teeth as there are on the wheel, so many turns
the screw has to make for the wheel to make one turn."

The deletion of the word "and" makes sense of the first part of the
passage; but the double mention of the movement of the tooth HṬ is
not convincing. We expect "and the point H comes into the place Ǧ,
and the tooth HṬ also into the place of the tooth ǦH."

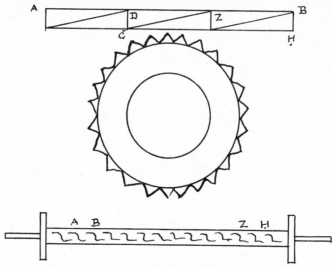

Fig. 28 b, the illustration for 2:18.
This figure is from the MS B. Some of the letters are lacking. The figure below the wheels seems to be meant to show that AB represents a screw. See text p. 76 sqq.

Fig. 28 a is taken from the Leiden MS.; it contains three separate figures, which I have numbered I, II, III. No. I no doubt is the original figure, where the screw is shown in the conventional way; but the scribe has been dissatisfied, because the teeth most obviously will not fit the screw. So he has made no. II, but even that has not satisfied him, and he has added no. III, in which the circle goes into the written text, but where the teeth engage the screw in the most convincing way.

Fig. 28 b is from the MS B. Here also the draughtsman has been dissatisfied with the screw; so he has drawn us a really fine screw below the wheel. All the letters on the wheel and some on the screw are lacking.

Pappos gives us the same explanation, p. 1114, but in his own words.

"... it is clear that for every turn of the screw one tooth is brought along; for Heron has shown this in his Mechanics, but we shall also write it down, so that we shall not have to seek anything outside this book". (See fig. 28 c).

"Let us imagine a screw AB, and the screw line on it AΓΔEZB, [and let these windings be imagined as single]. Let there be placed near it a toothed wheel HΓEΘ, having the teeth HΓ, ΓE, EΘ engaging the screw, the others then do not engage the rest of the windings. If we now turn the screw till the point E is moved towards the place of Γ, then E will fall on Γ, when the screw has made a full turn, and the tooth ΓE will take the place of ΓH, EΘ that of ΓE, and once

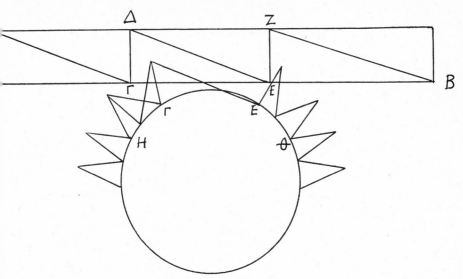

Fig. 28c, illustrating 2:18.
This figure, taken from the Vatican MS, shows Pappos's version of the cog-wheel engaging a screw. The explanation is given in the text p. 78 sq.

more EΘ, which has reached the place ΓE, will by one turn of the screw move its own length. And we have to imagine the same thing about the rest of the teeth, so that as many teeth as has the wheel, so many times the screw will have to move to cause one revolution of the wheel".

Fig. 28c is taken from the Vatican MS (89). The screw **AB** is shown in the conventional way, and a very long tooth, ΓE, is shown engaged in the furrow ΓΔE. But the rest of the teeth are shown narrow and pointed; the figure is on its way to become like Heron's No. I.

Fig. 28d shows how the figure must have looked originally; it is taken from a Parisian MS of Pappos (89). Between H and Θ there is a blot, but it is impossible to put in a letter, for there must be room for both Γ and E between H and Θ, so one of these letters will have to be moved one tooth.

"⟨19⟩ When the screw is turned, it moves the piece of wood that is called *ṭûlus*, as have said already, and it lifts the weight in a straight line; and this *ṭûlus* must, when the screw is not moved, stay securely and solidly in its place by a power which is in itself, and it must not be so that, when the screw is at rest from turning, the weight overcomes it, I mean that when this block is fitted into the screw furrow and is like a support for it, then it does not slip out of the screw furrow,

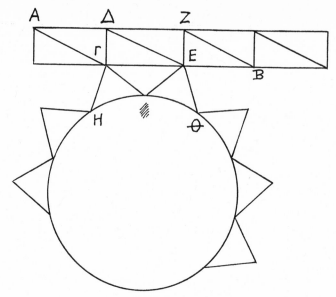

Fig. 28 d, illustrating 2:18.
This is another version of the cog-wheel engaging a screw, taken from a Pappos MS in the Bibliothèque Nationale in Paris. See the text p. 79. It is probably the original of the figures 28 a, b, c.

because if it does slip out, the whole weight will go down to the place from which it was lifted. And this block does not slip from the screw furrow when the end of the block is prepared for the furrow, and the furrow is like a greave for it, and we must form the screw furrows near each other, so that they become as if they were parallel to the basis of the cylinder on which the screw is traced. And if the windings are like this they will be like a greave to the block that lifts the weight". (ةlـمـ probably is a translation of κνημίς, which means a greave or a half-boot. Nix translates "Stiefel", but I think that the idea is that of a groove fitting the block as a greave fits the shin.) "If, however, the screw windings which are in the screw furrow are very steep, so that they seem to be parallel to the side of the cylinder, then the block that is called *ṭûlus*, if a heavy burden is hung from it, or a strong power overburdens it, will make the turning of the screw go backwards, and will make it turn the opposite way of the way it first turned. And from this it is evident to us that the screw can move the block called *ṭûlus* and that it also can be moved by this block; and it moves the block, if its screw furrow has its windings close together, and then it keeps its place when the screw is not turned, and the burden will stay suspended from it. But if the screw furrow is very steep and it does not stay when the screw is not turned, then the block will be that which turns the screw, because if a rope is wound the screw somewhere outside the furrowed part and if a weight is tied to the end of this rope, and the screw furrow is very steep, then if we move the block that is called *ṭûlus* upwards, we lift also the weight, and when we cease to lift the block, the weight will be at rest and remain suspended, because this block stops the screw furrow when the furrow is almost parallel to the side of the cylinder; and if there is no screw furrow on the cylinder, but just a furrow like a canal on one of the sides of the cylinder, then the block that is called *ṭûlus* will be a strong hindrance for this furrow like a canal; and if the screw windings are near each other and we lift the piece of wood that is called *ṭûlus*, then we do not move the weight, unless the power that lifts the *ṭûlus* is very great. And in the case that the weight is hanging from the *ṭûlus* and the screw turns are near each other and we turn the screw, the weight is lifted, and when we stop turning the screw, the weight is at rest and stays suspended; and if the screw turns are steep, then we do not move the weight unless there is a strong power compelling the screw. And now we have said enough about the screw and its use."

There seems to be something amiss with the text at the beginning of this chapter, for the shape of the top of the block and its fitting into the furrow do not depend on the grade of the screw. Two different things have been mixed together, first, that unless the *tylos* has a good grip on the screw, it cannot hold the burden at all; next, that the grade of the screw determines whether the burden will stay put when the screw is released, or whether it will make the screw turn backwards. According to Oreibasios, a lenticular screw was used for the screw and cog-wheel, but a square-threaded screw for a *tylos*. (See p. 171.) It is possible that the first part of the chapter has told us that the screw furrow should be square in cross section, like a canal; but I cannot see my way to restore the text.

"⟨20⟩ That the five powers that move the weight are like the circles round a single centre, this is clear from the figures that we have drawn in the preceding chapters. But I think that their shape is nearer to that of the balance than to the shape of the circle, because in the beginning the first explanation of the circles came from the balance. For here it was shown that the ratio of the weight hung from the smaller arm to that hung from the greater arm is like the ratio of the larger part of the balance to that of the smaller.

Now to all these five powers there comes a hindrance in their function if we want to move by them a great burden by a small power. As for the first three, it happens with them that we increase their size in proportion to the increase of the weight that we want to move by them, I mean the wheel on the axle, and the lever, and the machine that is called the many for lifting; as for the two remaining, I mean those that have a wedge and those that have a screw, we have to decrease their size in this proportion. And an example of this is if we want to move a weight of one thousand talents by a power corresponding to five talents, and we perform the movement by the axle with a wheel on it, then the line from the centre of the wheel to its circumference must be two hundred times the line going from

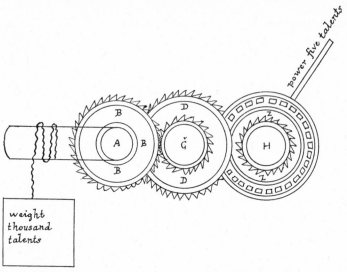

Fig. 29a, the illustration for 2:21-22. The figure is taken from the MS L. (3:4). The engine has been folded down, so that the drum with the rope is seen from the side. In the last wheel the square holes are holes in the rim for the handspakes. See text pp. 51 and 82 sqq.. For the shape of the teeth see p. 200. Cf. figs. 29b and c.

the centre of the axle to its circumference, and a little more than that. And if we perform this with the lever, we must have the greater part of it, where is the power that moves the weight, to be in this proportion or a little more; and to perform this by instruments of this sort is difficult or nearly impossible, because if we make the dimensions of the axle half an ell so that it is strong enough for the burden to be hung from it, then we shall have to make the diameter of the wheel one hundred ells or a little more, and this is a difficult job; and the same will be the case with the lever and the engine of the many for lifting, because we cannot make the proportions of the lever like that, and we cannot use many pulleys in this proportion. So let us contrive to overcome the difficulties that are inherent in these three powers."

The verb احتيال generally means to be cunning, crafty; here it is probably a translation of μηχανάομαι, which may mean that, but also quite neutrally to contrive, especially by mechanical means.

"⟨21⟩ We contend that the circle is of all the shapes the one with the greatest movement and ease, whether it is a circle moving round a single centre or moving along a surface at right angles to it. And so the shapes that are near it, I mean the balls and the cylinders, their movement is a turning, as we have explained in the preceding book.

Let us suppose that we wish first to move a great weight by means of the axle that goes through the wheel" (i.e. a windlass) "with a small power, and not come up against this difficulty in the arrangement. And let the weight we wish to move be for instance one thousand talents, and the power by which we wish to move it be five talents. Then we have first of all to get the power to balance the weight, because when this is evident" (Nix: when this has taken place) "we shall be able to make the power overcome the weight by some small addition which we make to the engine." (See fig. 29 a) "Now let the axle round which is wound the rope that is tied to the weight be at A, and let the wheel fastened to it be at B; and to make the construction (Nix: description) of the engine more easy, let us make the diameter of the wheel five times the diameter of the axle; so it is now necessary that the power that moves the wheel B to balance the weight of one thousand talents should be two hundred talents; but the power we are supposed to have is five talents only, so we are not able to move the given weight by the wheel B with this power. Let us then make an axle with teeth, and that is the axle Ǧ, and let it engage teeth in the wheel B, so that it will be so that when the axle Ǧ is moved, the wheel B is moved by its movement, together with the axle first supposed, and so it will be so that when the axle Ǧ is moved, the given weight is moved. And this axle will be moved by the same power that moves the axle B, † for we have proved that everything that is moved about a special centre is moved by a small power †. And therefore there is no difference between the moving of the weight by the wheel B and its moving by the axle Ǧ. And let there be also on the axle Ǧ a wheel fixed on it, and that is the wheel D, and let its diameter be e.g. five times the diameter of the axle Ǧ. Then the power on the wheel D to balance the weight must be forty talents; and we also make another axle and that is the axle H, engaging the wheel, then the moving power at H will also be forty talents; and so let there be a wheel fixed to the axle H, and that is the wheel Z, and let its diameter be eight times the diameter of the axle H, for the power of forty talents is eight times the power of five talents; and then the power which is at the wheel Z, which balances the weight of one thousand talents, will be five talents, and that was what was given. And in order to make the power overcome the weight we have to make the wheel Z a little larger or make the axle H a little smaller, and if we do that, the power will overcome the weight. And when we want to arrange several axles and wheels for this work, we have to use this ratio for it; for if we want to arrange for the power to balance the weight, we have to have the whole ratio to balance the weight. And if we want to overcome the burden, we have to add to the sum of the ratio something above the balance of the burden.

The axle that goes through the wheel moves the given weight in this way. And if we do not want to use toothed wheels, we wind ropes round the axles and wheels, and the work is done for us, because the last wheel that is moved will move the first axle which lifts the weight. And this shape, which consists of axles and wheels, is in solid posts with holes in them to take the ends of the axles; and when the burden is lifted, these posts must be placed in a solid and hard place."

This is the chapter from which is taken the construction of the so-called barulkos, which has been discussed on p. 22 sqq.

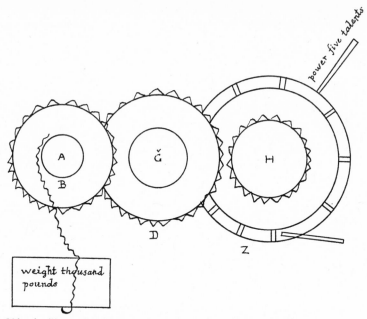

Fig. 29b, the illustration for 2:21-22. This is my rendering of the figure in the MS B, reproduced here as fig. 27c. See text below.

The text between the † † gives no sense.

It is interesting to see that Heron does not here mention the arrangement of the axles in a chest, as in the barulkos; but when he has described the same construction, but with ropes for cog-wheels, he adds that the engine should be set up in a firm piece of ground. The explanation is that the cog-wheels are merely a theoretical construction, while the pulleys with the ropes were really used.

Fig. 29a is taken from the MS L. We see clearly two pinions and three wheels; the first wheel is fixed on a drum, shown from the side, with the rope round it. In the last wheel the square holes for the hand-spakes are meant to be in the felloe, cf. the drawing of the felloe in fig. 14.

Fig. 29b is taken from the MS B. It is not so carefully made; the middle pinion has no teeth, and the holes in the felloe have become slots; the weight is given in pounds in stead of talents. The rope goes partly round the axle of the first wheel.

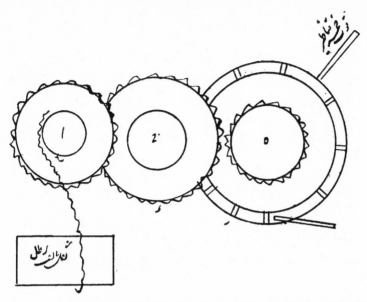

Fig. 29c, the illustration for 2:21-22. This is a photographic reproduction of the figure copied as fig. 29b. See text below.

Fig. 29c is a photographic reproduction of the same figure as fig. 29b, from the MS B, fol. 30v. It is given here to allow the reader to compare one of my renderings with the original. The letters on the figure are ١, ب, ج, د, ه, ز. See p. 20.

All these figures are discussed on p. 170 in connexion with the ships' hodometer; the figure given by Carra de Vaux and Nix is shown as fig. 63c. The difference in the shape of the teeth is discussed on p. 200.

"⟨22⟩ In these tools and their like with great power there will come a delay, because in proportion of the weakness of the moving power to the great size of the weight moved, in this proportion we need time, and the proportion of power to power and time to time is the same. For instance, when the power at the wheel B is two hundred talents and the weight is moved, the rope that is wound round A will need to be wound one turn for the weight to be moved, by the movement of the wheel B, to the extent of the circumference of A. But if the moving is done by the wheel D, it is necessary that the wheel Ğ is moved five times for the axle A to be moved once, because the diameter of the wheel B is five times the diameter of the axle Ğ, and so five times Ğ equals one time B, if we let the axles be equal, and the wheels. And if not, we find a similar proportion. The wheel D moves with B and the five circumferences that are by D will give five times the time for one circumference, and the two hundred talents are five times forty talents. And so the proportion of the moving power to the power moved is inverse †; and the same thing happens with many axles and many wheels, and it is proven like this."

When we read in the beginning that "the proportion of power to power and time to time is the same", we learn later that the proportion is inverse. Only here there seems to be something lacking. Nix translates: "Daher ist das Verhältnis der bewegenden Kraft zur Zeit ein umgekehrtes", but the word "time" is not in the text; it speaks of power only. Carra de Vaux, who has the same text, translates: "Ainsi le rapport du poids à la force motrice est égal à l'inverse du rapport d'ensemble des arbres et des tambours, quelque nombreux qu'ils soient," which gives excellent sense, but does not fit the text. I think it is necessary to add some words: "... is the inverse ⟨of the proportion of time to time⟩".

"⟨23⟩ Now we have to move the same weight by the same power by the engine that is called the many for lifting." (See fig. 30.) "Let the weight be where is the point A, and let the place from which it is lifted be where is the point B, and the place to which it is drawn be where is the point Ğ, and this is the solid beam, towards which we want to lift the weight. And let there be for instance five pulleys, and let the pulley from which the weight is drawn be at the point D; then the power that is at D to balance the thousand talents must be two hundred talents; but the power we are supposed to have is just five talents. So let us lead from the pulley D a rope towards an engine many for lifting which is at H, and let a solid beam be opposite it at Z, and let this solid beam and what belongs to it be at H, for instance having five pulleys, and let that which is drawn be at Ḥ; then the power which is at Ḥ must be a power of forty talents. So we again pass the end of the rope that is at Ḥ to another pulley which is at Ṭ, and let the solid beam be at K, and let the pulling be at K; then, since the forty talents are eight times five talents, the many for lifting must have eight pulleys, and then the power that is at K and which balances the thousand talents will be five talents. But for the power that is at K to overcome the weight, the pulleys have to be more than eight, and then the power will overcome the weight."

The figure in MS L is incomplete and rather poor; fig. 30 is taken from MS B. The course of the ropes is not correct, and the first pulley on the solid beam is superfluous. The scribe has been dissatisfied with the result; he has turned the drawing and put in some of the letters of reference, and added comments, in a rather indistict hand; one word I have been unable to read. The burden has "pounds" for "talents", as in fig. 29 b. The dotted line indicates the edge of the page.

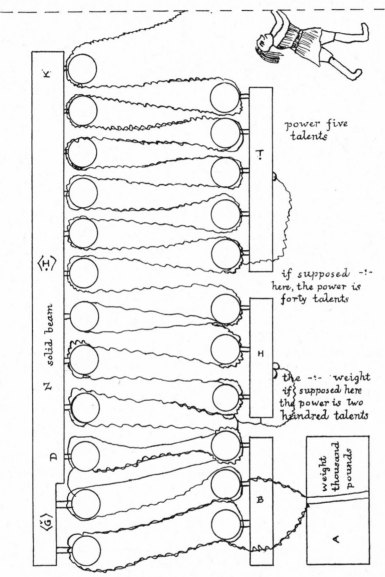

Fig. 30, illustrating 2:23-24. It is taken from the MS B, (3:4), and shows how to lift 1000 talents (not pounds!) with a power of 5 talents by means of a compound pulley with two whips. See text p. 86 sqq.

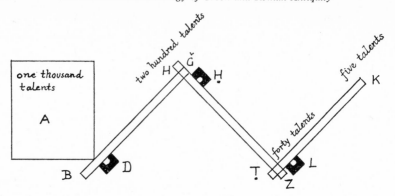

Fig. 31, the illustration for 2:25–26. The figure is taken from the MS L; see text p. 88 sq.

"⟨24⟩ That the delay will also be found in this tool is evident, because this works in the same proportion. The power that is at D which is two hundred talents, if it lifts the weight from B to Ğ, will have to wind five ropes stretching towards five pulleys the distance that is between the points BĞ, and the power that is at Ḥ has to wind up the five ropes five times, and if we make the distance BĞ, HZ equal, then by the winding of one rope of the ropes that are the distance BĞ there will be wound up five ropes of the ropes that are in the distance HZ, because if the weight is moved the distance that is between BĞ, there must be wound up for it five ropes of the size of the distance BĞ; and the proportion of time to time is like the proportion of the moving power to the moving power. Lest the increase in the ropes get too great, it is necessary that the distance HZ is five times the distance BĞ, and ṬK eight times HZ. And by this arrangement the many pulleys for lifting lift together."

"⟨25⟩ As for the lever, the same weight is moved by the same power by this arrangement:" (See fig. 31.) "let the weight be at the point A, and let the lever be BĞ, and let the stone that is under the lever be at the point D, and let the moving of the weight by the lever take place while it is parallel to the ground, and let ĞD be five times DB; then the power that is at Ğ, which balances the thousand talents, is two hundred talents. Let there now be another lever, which is HZ, and let the point H be the one at the head of the lever, engaging the point Ğ, so that Ğ is moved by the moving of H, and let the stone that is under the lever be at the point Ḥ, and let it be moved towards D, and let ZḤ be five times ḤH; then the power that is at Z will be forty talents. Let there be another lever, which is ṬK, and let us place the point Ṭ on the point Z, and let it be moved in the opposite direction of H. And let the stone that is under the lever be at the point L, and let it be moved the way in which the point H is not moved, and let KL be eight times LṬ; then the power that is at K will be five talents, and it will balance the weight. And if we want the power to overcome the weight, we shall have to make KL more than eight times LṬ; but if KL is eight times LṬ and ZD five times ḤH and ĞD more than five times DB, the power will overcome the weight."

Fig. 31 is taken from MS L.

"⟨26⟩ And in this the delay will be found in the same proportion, because there is no difference between these levers and the axles that go into the wheels turning on centres. For these levers are like the axles moving on the points DḤL, which are the stones on which the levers turn, and the circles of the axles are the circles described by the points BHṬ; and the wheels are the circles described by the points ǦZK; and just as we have proved for these axles that the proportion of the power to the power is like the proportion of the time to the time, so we prove it also here."

"⟨27⟩ About the wedge and the screw, we cannot say the same, because as we have explained before, no hindrance is found in them, but the opposite; and every time we increase the power that is in those two, each of them will grow smaller. Our intention was, however, to contrive for those engines, whose size increases like the increase of the weight, that we should be able to do the work with smaller engines, and so make it easier. And so it was not necessary in the wedge and the screw to contrive to make them smaller in order to make the work easy."

"⟨28⟩ But that the delay is also found to take place in those two, that is evident, since many blows take more time than a single blow, and the turning of the screw many times takes more time than a single turn. And we have proved that the proportion of the angle to the angle of the wedge is like the proportion of the moving blow to the moving blow; and so the proportion of the time to the time will be like the proportion of the power to the power."

The discussion of the wedge and the screw is found in 2:15, 17, 19; see p. 72 sq, 76 sq, 79 sqq.

"⟨29⟩ In the preceding we have moved the given weight by many axles through wheels and by many levers and by many pulleys; but we can move the given weight by a combination of those, and by combining them with each other, apart from the wedge, because that alone is only moved by blows. Let us now explain that we can put together the four powers and by their combination move the given weight." (See fig. 32.) "Let the given weight be at the point A, and let there be a lever at the points BǦ, and let the point B be the end of the lever that is under the burden, and the point Ǧ be lifted, and let the stone on which the lever moves be the point D, and let ǦD be five times DB; then the power that is at Ǧ will be two hundred talents to balance the weight A. And let us fasten to the end of the lever which is the point Ǧ an engine many-for-lifting, which is by the point H, and let the other engine that is parallel to it be at a solid beam, and that is by the point Z, and let the thing (?) that pulls this engine be by the point Ḥ (MS: Ǧ) and let it have five pulleys; then the pulling power will be forty talents. And let there be an axle in a wheel, and that is ṬK, and the mark Ṭ is on the axle and the mark K is on the wheel, and let the rope that comes from the pulley be wound round the axle, and let the wheel with teeth be at right angles to the given surface, and let a screw be engaged in its teeth, and that is the screw L, and let there be on it a handle to turn it at the point M, and let the teeth be

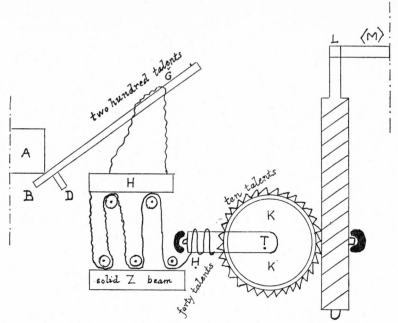

Fig. 32, the illustration for 2:29. The figure is taken from the MS L. (3:4) See text
p. 89 sqq.

engaged in the screw furrow. If we now turn the handle M, the screw L turns,
and the wheel K turns by the turning of the screw, and by this turning the axle
Ṭ turns, and the rope that is on the pulleys is wound up on it; and it presses down
the end of the lever Ğ, and the weight is lifted. Let the diameter of the wheel
K be four times the diameter of the axle Ṭ, so that the power which is by L will
be ten talents, and let the handspake M be twice the diameter of the screw cylinder,
and then the power which is at M that balances the thousand talents will be five
talents. And if we increase the handspake that is at the point M by a certain
increase, the power that is five talents will prevail. As for the axle that is in the
wheel and the screw, they move in a firm support in the shape of a chest, so that
the ends of the axle can be in two vertical sides of the support, and the lower
end of the screw can turn in the bottom of the firm support, and its upper end
in the middle of the upper surface. And we prolong its end and place on it a
wheel in which the handspake is placed. And this support like a chest should
be in a firm place, in a place strong in its foundations, solidly built. When the
handspake is turned, the weight is lifted."

Fig. 32 is taken from the Leiden MS. The left side of the weight A
and the end of the handle on the screw are cut off by the edge of the
page; the letter M is lacking.

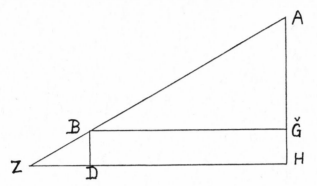

Fig. 33, the illustration for 2:30, 31. The figure is taken from the MS L. See text p. 91 sq.

The computation of the power of this engine confirms the suspicion roused by the *Barulkos* (see p. 27) that Heron did not know how to compute the power of the endless screw. Here he needs a power of 10 talents at the circumference of the wheel K, and makes the proportion of the handle M to the radius of the screw 2:1 in order to reduce the 10 talents to 5. But he disregards entirely the part played by the screw. The wheel is shown with 32 teeth. Making the radius of the wheel equal to the length of the handle, we find that one turn of the wheel equals 32 turns of the handle, a gear of 1:32 in stead of the 1:2 supposed by Heron. To reach our target, 1:200, we need one reduction of 1:5 and another of 1:2 to have power to spare for moving the weight. With 40 teeth on the wheel and a proportion of 1:5 between axle and wheel, the endless screw would do the work alone.

It is evident that this combination of four powers, like the combinations of the single powers, is merely a theoretical example. At this time the endless screw was not used for cranes and hoists. In stead of multiplying the engines, the contractors would multiply the man power: what one worker could not do, was done by ten or twenty or forty workers pulling together under the command of an overseer.

"⟨30⟩ As for the wedge and the screw, we use this procedure." (See fig. 33.)
"The angle of the wedge that we want to use is the angle ABǦ, and it is acute. Now I contend that the wedge whose edge is more acute moves the weight by smaller blows, I mean by less power, and it may reach the point of smallness where it will not work because of its acuity. Let there be drawn a line at right angles to the line BǦ, and that is the line BD, to make the wedge stronger. And let there be drawn a line parallel to the line ǦB, and that is the line DH. And

let us draw from the point H a line parallel to the upright, and that is the line HǦ. And let there be formed a wedge like the given one, and that is ABDH. Let the side that is BD be inserted, so that a small part of it (i.e. the wedge) is under the burden. And let its head be AH. Then it is evident for us that the wedge ABǦ, if it is hammered, will drive in ABDH. The proof of this is that we draw two lines AB, DH towards Z; then the edge AZH will be the same as ABǦ, and AZH will also be a wedge that is able to be moved by this power. Now let us imagine that which is near the points BZD to be beneath the burden; then the wedge will have penetrated so far. As for the wedge, this is the proof. And it is not absolutely necessary that we make the edge of the wedge acute, because we have already shown that every slight blow is able to move every wedge, if it is made many times; and we make smaller angles just for the sake of the small blows. And thus it is not absolutely necessary that we use small angles for the wedge."

Fig. 33 is taken from the Leiden MS.; it illustrates both ch. 30 and ch. 31.

Heron has already shown, ch. 15, 17, 19, 27, that to get a greater effect out of the wedge, we have to make the angle more acute; here he warns us that we may go too far. Then he shows that if we make the wedge larger without altering the angle, nothing happens at all: it is still the same wedge.

As for making the angle more acute, it will result in lighter blows in greater number; but the same result may be obtained by heavier blows, without altering the angle.

"⟨31⟩ As for the screw, we can [not]" (del. C. de V. & Nix) "proceed in the same way, and for this it is necessary to place on the angle of the screw turn, which is the angle ABǦ, an upright AǦ at right angles to BǦ, equal to the thickness of the *ṭûlus* which we want to engage in the screw furrow, and to make a cylinder whose circumference equals the line BǦ, and to draw a screw line from these lines at the distance AǦ, and cut out the screw line, when its distance will be equal to AǦ; and in this way we are able to fit the piece of wood into the screw furrow."

It is rather queer how difficult it is to decide whether the "not" in the first sentence should be kept or deleted. Carra de Vaux deleted it; Nix kept it in his text, but deleted it in his list of corrections. The fact is that it is impossible to find any connexion between the chapter on the wedge and the chapter on the screw, except that the figure is the same. The only thing Heron tells us is how to make a screw to fit a given *tylos*. It looks as if the *tylos* had to fit into a lentil-shaped furrow; otherwise the distance AǦ would have to be twice the thickness of the *tylos*.

"⟨32⟩ Since we have now explained for each of these powers that it is possible by a known power to move a known weight, it is necessary also to explain, that if it were possible that all the parts made were turned accurately, of equal weight, with parts of the same smoothness, then it would be possible with each of these engines to perform the work we have described in the given proportion. But since it is not possible for man to make them perfect in smoothness and uniformity, it is necessary to increase the power on account of what may occur of roughness in the engines, and we must make them greater, and so we increase their size above the proportion we have first given, so that no hindrance occurs herein, and what we find by the use of the engines shall not make out wrong what was correct in our theoretical proof."

For "(turned) accurately" the MSS have بالشهد, which Carra de Vaux translates "parfaitement". Nix does not accept "bear witness" in this sense; he corrects it to بالمبرد, "with the file." But neither the correction nor the sense appeals to me, so I suggest بالسداد, "with accuracy".

Heron has now finished the theoretical explanation of his five powers; in ch. 33–34 he turns to a collection of mechanical puzzles, many of which are dealt with in the Mechanical Problems of Aristoteles. It looks as if it was necessary for any teacher of mechanics to show his scholars how these questions are to be answered. In a long introduction Heron explains that questions are asked when the cause and effect are not clearly perceived; but to explain the phenomena we must start out from known and accepted physical and mechanical principles, and show how they work in the case in question. But often the explanation will make us wonder, because it looks like the opposite of what we thought was the case.

He calls special attention to the fact that when a great burden is moved, it is because it has been divided between many small powers. If one man cannot move a stone, two men can move it; when many men perform a piece of work together, each one gets only a share; if everybody had the whole work to do, it would be impossible. I wonder what sort of sophism is answered by this statement of a most obvious fact.

The problems and their solutions do not give us any information about the mechanical technology of the time; I shall give only the one answer that corresponds to the Aristotelean problem no. 21, which is given here on p. 16.

"⟨34⟩ 9. Why is the drawing of teeth performed with a forceps and not with the hand? Because we cannot grasp the tooth with the whole hand, but only with part of it, and just as it is more difficult for us to lift a weight with two fingers only than with the whole hand, so also to grasp and press the tooth with two fingers is more difficult than with the whole hand, since in either case the power is the same; and the division of the forceps on its nail also gives the hand power over the tooth, because it is a lever, where the hand is on the longer part; and the distance (i.e. the length) of the forceps helps in moving the tooth, and that is because the root of the tooth is that on which the lever moves. And because the length of the forceps is greater than the root of the tooth, on which something great is moved, the hand prevails over the power that is in the root, since there is no difference between the moving of a weight and the moving of a power equal to that weight. And when we close the hand that was open, a resistance comes not from the weight of the hand, but from the power with which the muscles keep together."

There seems to be a distinct progress both in the theory and the practice of the use of the forceps between the time of the Mechanical Problems and Heron's time.

The rest of Book 2 is given over to statical problems: finding the centre of gravity in a triangle, a quadrangle and a polygon, or computing the distribution of weight in similar figures supported by their angles and carrying a weight in an arbitrary point.

Book 3

The third Book describes the accessories necessary for the practical use of the five powers; some chapters on presses are added, because here also great power is needed.

"⟨1⟩ In the preceding Book we have spoken of the five powers and we have explained the engines by which the great weights are moved by a small power; and we have, in our opinion, proved more than those that came before us; and we have explained the reason why the delay will accompany the engines of great power; and we have explained other things of use for the students about equilibrium and pressure, in which there is enough for the students. In this Book we describe engines that are useful to make that easier whose existence and use has already been described, which also help in the moving of the heavy bodies; and we also explain the engines that are used for pressing, because these also need a great power when they are used.

The things that are moved along the ground are moved on tortoises, and a tortoise is a solid body made of a square piece of wood whose ends are turned upwards."

This passage has been discussed in detail on p. 50 sqq. The Greek text has "square pieces of timber" in the plural.

> "And on these engines the burdens are placed, and in their ends ropes are tied, or something else to be pulled, by which the tortoises are dragged along. And these ropes are either pulled by the hands or by some other bodies (?). And when the ropes are pulled, the tortoises slide along the ground. And there are placed under the tortoises round, thin sticks, or else boards, for the tortoises to move on. If the burden is small, it is necessary to use the round sticks, and when the weight is great, it is necessary to use the boards, because they do not move quickly; and this is because the round sticks, if they roll under the burden, are crushed under the burden because of the violence of the speed of the movement. And some people place neither boards nor round sticks, but put strong wheels on the ends of the tortoises, so that they move on these."

The "other bodies" is a queer expression. I cannot imagine the word σῶμα in the Greek text. Pappos has simply "winches". But mules or oxen are a possibility.

Pappos has excerpted this part of the Mechanics, p. 1130:

> "In the following we shall describe, out of Heron's third Book, engines built for ease and usefulness, by which also great burdens are moved.
> The things that are moved along the ground, he says, are dragged on tortoises. The tortoise is a frame put together of square timbers with upturned noses. On these, then, the weights are placed, and to their ends are tied either compound pulleys or the ends of ropes. These are then either pulled by hand or go to winches, and when these are turned, the tortoise slides along the ground, with rollers or boards placed under it. For if the burden is small, you have to use rollers, but if it is larger, boards, because they do not slide easily. For the turning rollers are dangerous, if the burden takes on speed. Some people use neither rollers nor boards, but drag by placing solid wheels on the tortoises."

Fig. 34 is taken from the Vatican MS of Pappos (89), for there is no figure in Heron for this chapter. It shows first a tortoise carrying a column, rolling on rollers, and pulled by a compound pulley, whose outer block is tied to a fixed place, while the rope goes to another fixed place. The two runners with the snub noses are held together by cross pieces, marked "yoke", with wedges. The column is lashed to the tortoise. The rollers do not seem to be indicated save by the inscription. The small squares on the upper runner may be meant for holes for the lashings; the cylinders shown above the pulley I cannot explain.

In the middle there is a tortoise with a square stone lashed to it; it slides along boards and is dragged by a rope tied to the foremost yoke and going by devious ways to a winch or capstan fastened to a

96

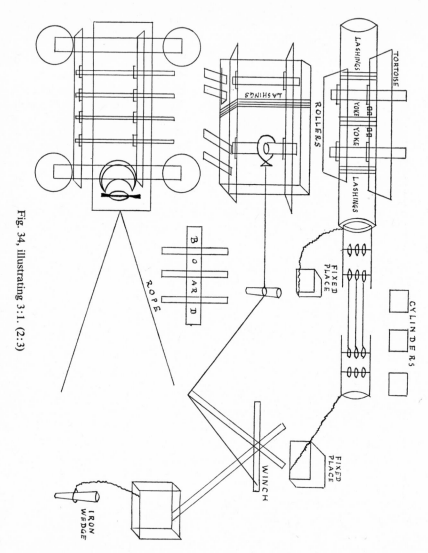

Fig. 34, illustrating 3:1. (2:3)

The figure is taken from Pappos, from the Vatican MS; it shows three different "tortoises" or sleds. The explanation is given in the text p. 95 sqq. The upper runner of the first tortoise has an inscription which neither I myself, using a photocopy, nor dr. Per Krarup, who kindly looked up the manuscript in Rome, was able to interpret.

fixed place, which again is anchored to an iron wedge. A small figure below and to the right seems to indicate that the board is placed along the route, and that the boards seen sticking out below the lower runner are cross boards fixed on the tortoise, to slide along the longitudinal boards.

The lowest figure shows a tortoise with four solid wheels; the runners are held together by four yokes with wedges. Two ropes are tied to a toggle or iron dog placed across a hole. The half moon I take to be an unsuccessful attempt to draw the hole. Since the square with the hole has no thickness, it is probably not a stone, but the bottom of the tortoise.

There is no doubt that Qusṭâ ibn Lûqâ and Pappos have had the same text; when the renderings differ, we expect Qusṭâ ibn Lûqâ to give a meticulous, word for word translation, while Pappos may be giving the sense in his own words. But about the danger of using rollers it seems that Pappos has followed Heron very closely. Heron, as we shall find in the following, always looks after the safety of his devices, which is why the rendering by Pappos rings true. Also the rollers will be crushed by the weight of the burden rather than by its speed. I suppose that Qusṭâ ibn Lûqâ has not understood the text and has supplied his own interpretation of the danger.

"⟨2⟩ For the lifting of the heavy things upwards there is also need for certain machines, and among these some have one mast, and some have two masts, and some have three, and some have four masts. As for the one that has a single mast it is made in this way." See fig. 35. "We take a long piece of wood, longer than the distance to which we want to lift the weight on it. Even though this pole is strong in itself, we take a rope and coil it round it, and we wind it at equal spaces, and the vertical line between the single windings may be four spans. The strength of the pole is increased, and the windings of the rope on it are like steps for anybody who has something to do at the top of the pole, and this makes the work easier. And if this pole is not strong in itself, we have to look to the amount of the weight that we want to lift, lest the power of the weight be greater than the strength of the mast. And we set up this mast straight on a piece of wood, so that it can move on it, and we fasten to the top of this post three or four ropes and lead then to very strong fixed posts, and we tie the ropes to these. Then we place on the top of this column pulleys which we tie to it with a rope, and we fasten the rope running over the pulleys to the burden that we wish to lift. Then we pull on the rope either by hand or with another engine, and so the burden is lifted. And if it is necessary to place the stone on a wall or some other place where we want it, we slacken the rope that is on one of the solid posts, those that hold the post on which the pulleys are tied, the one that is on the opposite side of the one towards which the stone is to be placed, and so this post will lean

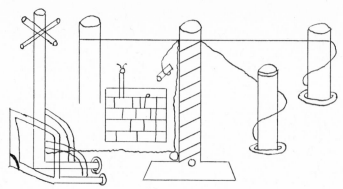

Fig. 35, the illustration for 3:2. The figure is taken from the MS L (3:4) and shows a one-mast crane. See text p. 97 sqq.

towards that side, and the rope running over the pulleys is slackened little by little towards the place on which we want to place it. But if the leaning of the post to which the pulley is tied does not succeed in bringing the lifted weight near the place we want, we place under it (the weight) rollers on which we can move it, or we push it with a lever till we get it into the place we want. When we have done this, we move the post back to its place on the other side, the one where we are. Then we make it fast again and work with it the same way as before."

Pappos has a description of the same crane p. 1132:

"For the burdens that are to be moved upwards, he says, there are engines, some with one mast, some with two masts, some with three masts, some with four masts.

Those with one mast are like this: We take a strong pole, longer than the way we want to lift the burden; and even if it is strong in itself, they wind a rope round it and tighten it with close windings. The distance between the windings should not be more than 4 spans (31 cm), and in this way both the pole is made stronger and the windings of the rope will be useful as steps for the workers and for those who want to get to the top. If the pole is not strong, it is put together of several pieces; you have to calculate the burden to be lifted, so that the mast is not too weak. The mast is now set up upright on a piece of wood, and from its head are tied some three or four ropes, which are stretched and made fast on some fixed places, so that the pole, no matter which way it gets a strain, will not yield, since it is held by the tight ropes. To its head they tie compound pulleys and make it fast to the burden; then they pull either by hand or by fastening it (the rope from the pulley) to capstans, until the burden is lifted. If the stone has to be placed on a wall or wherever you like, they slacken one of the ropes tied to the top, the one on the side away from the burden, and incline the mast, and placing the rollers under the burden in the part where the sling is not wound round the stone, they slacken the ropes of the compound pulleys, until the burden comes to rest on the rollers; then they take out the sling and lever the burden along, until they have brought it to the place they want. Then they drag the board under the mast by hand with a rope and bring it to another part of the building, slackening the stays the while, and then once more they make them fast and use the engine as described before."

The Arabic version and that of Pappos agree very well until we get to the last few sentences. It seems more likely that Pappos should have elaborated the directions than that Quṣṭā ibn Lūqā should have simplified them; but I do not venture to decide the question.

We here get an insight into Quṣṭā ibn Lūqā's way of translating. For the Greek κῶλον, literally "leg", he writes قائمة, "an upright" (mast); for ξύλον, "wood", he has the first time خشبة, "piece of wood", next عود, "wood", "timber" (pole), but then he changes it to ركن, "support", "pillar" (post), because he wants to use the same word for the "fixed places" for the staying ropes.

Fig. 35 is taken from the Leiden MS. It shows in the middle the mast standing on its square of wood. The circle near its foot may be meant for a pivot for it to turn on, but there is no indication of planks to hold the pivot, and for a crane with a single mast it would be better just to round off the lower end and place it in a hollow in the board; it could then turn to all sides. From the top of the mast stays are going to three fixed posts, as thick as is the mast, and also round in cross section; two of them are shown to be placed in holes in the ground. A small column is being lifted on to a wall, where another column is already in place. The burden is held by a single rope, which from the top of the mast, where no pulley is shown, runs down to a pulley at its foot, and so on to a capstan. The construction of the capstan has baffled the scribe, but it would seem that the circles round two of the horizontal planks indicate that they were placed in holes in the ground.

The mast shows apparently a rope wound round it in an open spiral, but I do not think that that is what is meant in the texts, for this rope would not strengthen the mast very much. We have to imagine the mast wound like a fishing-rod, with many separate windings of four or five close turns; these single windings then should be 31 cm apart.

"⟨3⟩ As for the engine that has two posts, it is made in this way. We take the implement that is called *audûs* (οὐδός, threshold) and place the two posts on it. And let them slope in the upper part with a slight slope, to the extent of one fifth of the distance at their feet. Then the two posts are made fast to the *audûs*, so that their two ends are joined, one to the other, and we place on the

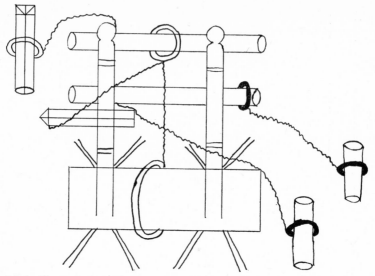

Fig. 36, the illustration for 3:3. The figure is taken from the MS L (3:4) and shows a crane with two masts. See text p. 99 sq.

ends of the two posts another cross-piece, on which there is fastened a pulley many-for-lifting, and let the other pulleys be fastened to the stone. Then we pull this rope as we did in the first case either by hand or by draught animals, and the weight is lifted. And to set up these two posts it is necessary that they are bound by ropes as we have described it before. Then we place the stone, and we move the *audûs* to the other side of the building, in so far as the necessity calls for it."

Fig. 36 is taken from the Leiden MS. It shows the two masts placed on a threshold; they do not slope towards one another, but are parallel. Two cross-pieces are shown, one above the other. Stays are going from the top of one mast, and from the ends of the lower cross-piece, towards three fixed posts. Eight double lines from the threshold probably indicate four struts for each of the masts. A rope is going from a ring round the threshold to a ring round the upper cross-piece, and from there to a square stone hanging in the air. The rings probably represent lashings to hold the pulleys. The rope from the lower pulley to the workers or the animals is lacking. Here, as in fig. 35, there is no attempt to show the compound pulley.

"⟨4⟩ As for the engine that has three posts, it is made in this way: We take three posts leaning against each other, and their ends are joined together in a

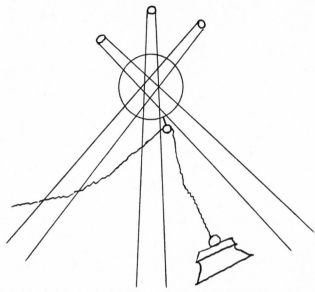

Fig. 37, the illustration for 3:4. The figure is taken from the MS L and shows quite clearly a crane in the shape of a tripod lifting a base for a column. See text p. 100 sq.

single point, and in this point in which the three posts are joined together we tie a pulley many-for-lifting, and the other part of it is tied to the burden; and when the rope from the pulley is drawn the burden is lifted. This implement has a stand more firm and steady than others, but it is not easy to use in any place we want, but the place to which we want to lift the burden is in the middle of this engine. So when we need to lift a burden to a place where we can set up this implement so that the place comes in the middle of it, we set it up there."

The Arabic word قاعدة means a base, and is certainly a translation of the Greek βάσις. I have used the word "stand", for that is how I should translate "basis" here. The next sentence is not quite clear; it means that the tripod cannot be used for taking up a burden and putting it down somewhere else; it will put down its burden in one place only.

Fig. 37 is taken from the Leiden MS. How anybody can have had the heart to redraw this charming little figure passes my comprehension.

"⟨5⟩ As for the engine that has four masts, it is made for the very great weights, and it is like this: four wooden posts are set up so that their arrangement is like the shape of a quadrangle with parallel sides, and in width it should be such that there is room to move the stone inside it and to lift it easily. Then we fasten

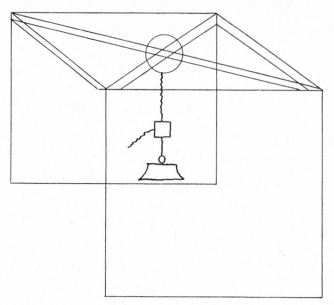

Fig. 38, the illustration for 3:5. The figure is taken from the MS L and shows a four-mast crane lifting a base for a column. There is a distinct attempt at perspective drawing. See text p. 101 sqq.

to the ends of these posts balks going from one to another, and this should be done skilfully and solidly. Then we arrange on these beams other beams and fasten them to each other with a fastening in a different arrangement, so that all the posts are joined together. Then we fasten the pulleys in the middle of these beams in the point where the balks come together. Then we make fast the stone in the rope that is over the pulleys, and we pull it, and the burden is lifted.

It is necessary in all mechanical engines that we guard against using nails or pegs; in short, whenever it is a question of weight, and especially of great weight, on the contrary we have to use ropes and cords and fasten by them what we want in stead of the thing that we want to put nails into."

There is some difficulty with the text. Carra de Vaux reads: خلفها كخلفة, translating "(poutres) disposées en forme (de carré)". Nix has: حلقتها كحلقة, translating: "in Form eines (viereckigen) Geheges (mit parallelen Seiten)". The MSS have: K حلقتها BCL خلفها; CKL كحلقة B الخلقة. Now خلفة means 1) difference 2) succeeding, which does not give much sense. Nix's حلقة means a circle, a ring, a hoop, and "a circle like a square circle with parallel sides" is not convincing. But خلقة "make, fashion, form" seems to fit the sense—which is obvious anyway. So I should read خلقتها كخلقة.

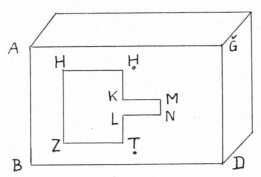

Fig. 39, the illustration for 3:6. The figure is taken from the MS L and shows the drawing on the stone for the undercut hole to take the hanger. See text p. 103 sq.

Fig. 38 is taken from the Leiden MS. It is rather sketchy, but shows quite plainly that the "different arrangement" of the second set of beams means a diagonal cross. There is a distinct attempt at true perspective in this figure, though it is not quite successful. Here at least the lower block of the compound pulley is indicated.

"⟨6⟩ Because it happens with the tool that looks like a sling by which the stone is lifted, that it hinders the placing of the stone in the place where it has to be placed, we make this implement, and that is what is called a hanger." (See fig. 39.) "We draw on the side of the stone, that is the surface ABǦD, a figure like the figure drawn. This is so that every one of its sides HZḤṬ, KLMN, is parallel to the sides; and let HZḤṬ be greater in breadth than KLMN; but as for their length, it should be the same. I mean that the line KM is equal to the line HḤ. Then we cut out this figure into the depth of the stone, and the depth of the cut should correspond to the weight of the stone. And let the cut of the surface HZḤṬ be at right angles to the horizon exactly; but for the figure KLMN, the cut is made sharp, I mean that the bottom is broader then the top, and it becomes a cut like a wooden key, where the narrow part is equal to KLMN, and the broad part is equal to HZḤṬ; and we make also like the wooden key a thing of iron which fits into this cut, with a ring fastened to it above; and it is inserted into the cut HZḤṬ so that it disappears into it. Then it is pushed and turned till it goes into the other cut and cannot come out. Then there is placed in the cut HZḤṬ wood so that the iron cannot be pushed out. Then we make fast in the ring that is fixed on the iron peg the rope that lifted the sling in which the stone was placed, and we lift in this way until it comes into the place we want, without any hindrance whatever. And when the stone is set down in its place, the pegs are removed and the iron is taken out, and then it is placed in another stone, which is also lifted."

Fig. 39 is taken from the Leiden MS. The stone is shown here in axonometry rather than perspective.

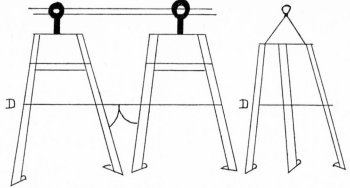

Fig. 40, the illustration for 3:7. The figure is taken from the MS L; (3:4) it shows two "crabs", that is grabs for lifting stones. See text p. 104 sq.

In Pappos, quoted here with ch. 3:2, p. 98 sq, the stone is carried by a sling, that is with ropes passing underneath; it has to be placed on rollers, so that the sling can be removed. But if the stone can be set down at once in its proper place, it is better to avoid ropes going round it.

The shape of the iron hanger is obviously that of a dove-tail tenon. The Arabic word قفل, meaning a lock or bolt, is certainly a translation of the Greek κλείς, a bolt, lock, clasp, hook, key, &c. It seems possible that Heron may have called a dove-tail tenon κλείς ξυλίνη.

This iron tenon is placed first into the square cut HZHT "so that it ... in it". The Arabic word يعبّر does not fit the obvious sense. I suggest يغرب, "disappear", tentatively.

The "wood" placed in the hole to keep in the iron dove-tail is in several pieces, as shown by the plural where it is taken out. Any small ends of boards would do, as long as they were wedged home.

"⟨7⟩ The stones are also lifted by the implements that are called the crabs, when ⟨...⟩ they have three or four legs, and their ends are bent so that they take the shape of hooks, and these hooks are placed on the sides of the burden. And there are placed on their ends cross-pieces, I mean on the ends of the legs, and they are tied with ropes, and then they are lifted, and the burden comes up. And it is necessary to place on the ends of the legs cross-pieces joined together outside the stone on their ends, so that it does not happen, when the stone is hanging from them and is lifted, that the stone falls down; but these cross-pieces are lashed to each other; and the ropes to the pulley are tied to them (the crabs) outside them (the lashings) and when they are pulled, the stone is lifted."

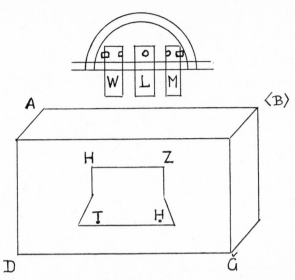

Fig. 41, the illustration for 3:8. The figure is taken from the MS L and shows the stone, the shape of the hole in the stone, and the three pegs to fit into the hole. See text p. 105 sq.

Fig. 40 is taken from the Leiden MS. It shows on the left a crab with four legs, arranged two and two; on the right is a crab with three legs, which must have been hinged to a triangular frame. The horizontal line with the letters D D I cannot explain. Since the claws are not self-acting, it would be necessary to secure their grip on the stone by boards or planks lashed together all round the stone. The ropes for lifting the burden must not be tied to the lashings.

I suppose that there is something missing in the first period, for the "when" gives no sense at all. You would expect "when ⟨the burden is to be placed on rollers.⟩ They have ...".

The word قائمة here is probably, as in 3:2, a translation of κῶλον, which here may be rendered as "leg".

"⟨8⟩ There is also made for this work another shape than that, and greater in reliability than that." (See fig. 41.) "Let the base of the stone be the one with ABǦD on it; then we cut out in it a hole like a rectangle, and that is HZḤṬ, and let it be of a suitable depth. And let its cut be slanting, on the sides, I mean that there is in it in the depth of the two sides a suitable undercut, and in this undercut it is strong enough to carry the stone which hangs by it. Then we make two pegs of iron, whose ends are bent like the shape of the letter *gamma*, and let there be in their tops a ring or a hole. Then we fit those two together into the side of the hole and we put their bend into the slant of the cut; and we use also another, third peg of iron, and fit it in between these two pegs to hinder these two pegs from being moved. And let also the third peg be pierced in the top by a hole that comes into line with the two holes in the two other pegs. And we fit into the three holes an axle whose one end is thick; and the three pegs will fill the cut HZḤṬ. And the bends of the pegs will go into the furrow which is in the two sides of the bottom of the cut; and the third peg will just fill out the space between the two pegs, and the three pegs will become as a single body. Then we fasten to the axle that goes through the three pegs the ropes that belong to a pulley, and there is on the top of the engine by which we lift the weight another pulley opposite the one that is on the stone; and the ropes are passed through it and they are pulled, and so the stone is lifted, because the middle peg will not let go of the two pegs with their curved ends inside the stone to hold it. So it is lifted until it comes over the place where we want to set it down, and it is let down in that place. And when the stone has come down on its place, the axle is taken out and the middle peg is taken out, and both the pegs with the bend ends are taken away. Then we make ready another stone and handle it the same way.

In this method we must guard against using too hard iron, lest it break, and we must guard against what is soft, lest it bend and twist because of the weight of the stone; but we use of it that which is in between, neither too hard nor too soft; and it is also necessary to guard against a bend in the iron and a fold in it or a crack that it has got when it was made. And the fault in it is serious, not only because the stone may fall, but because it may hit the workers, if it falls."

Fig. 41 is taken from the Leiden MS. It shows the stone, axonometrically, the hole in the stone, in a vertical cut, and the hanger. The bends on the two outer pegs are not shown; the squares and circles on the pegs probably indicate the holes. There are no letters in the text corresponding to the W, L, M on the pegs. The curved handle for the axle is not mentioned, either.

The remarks about the sort of iron to use are interesting. What is meant is that we should use steel, not glass-hard steel, which will break, and not just iron, which will bend, but hardened and tempered steel, free from flaws. We may note also the concern for the safety of the workers.

Heron has now finished his description of the ordinary ways of transport and proceeds to instruct his scholars in some special methods used to meet special cases.

"⟨9⟩ As for the ways in which we lift or hoist the heavy things, they are those that we have described; but we may have to contrive ways, with due regard to the place and the time and the need, also without these implements, and we shall now explain how we must proceed in each of these cases.

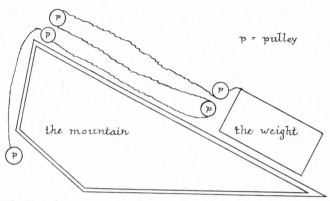

Fig. 42, the illustration for 3:9. The figure is taken from the MS B; no corresponding figure is found in the MS L. It shows a stone block being let down a mountain road. See text below.

Some people use for bringing down very great stones from the top of high mountains an arrangement so that the stone shall not, because of the slope of the mountain, roll down by its own fall (?) and strike the animals that drag it, and the carts, and destroy them. So they use two roads on the mountain in the place where they want to bring down the stones, from the top to the bottom, and make them just as easy as possible, and they take two carts with four wheels and bring one of them to the top of the road along which they want to bring down the stone, and the other to the bottom of the other road. Then they fasten to a solid post between the two roads a pulley and bring a rope from the cart that carries the stone to the pulley and take it to the other cart that is below; and they place in this cart that is below small stones, such fragments as come off the very big stones, until they give it a weight less (?) than the stone they want to bring down. Then they hitch draught-animals to this cart to drag it upwards, and by the mounting of this cart little by little the very large stone will come down softly and little by little also."

Fig. 42 is taken from the MS B; no such figure is found in the MS L. It is not very illustrative.

"⟨10⟩ Some people want to lift by this method also very great columns, so as to put them down on their bases in the place they want, by the following arrangement:" See fig. 43. "They tie to the top of the column they want to lift ropes and take them to pulleys made fast on a solid tower, and take them through till they come out on the other side of the pulleys. Then they tie to the ends that go through the pulleys receptacles, in which there can be placed stones and heavy things, I mean something like chests or some other thing that resembles them. Then they place in these receptacles suitable stones and weights, till they equal the weight of the column, and overcome it; and hereby they lift it and it comes

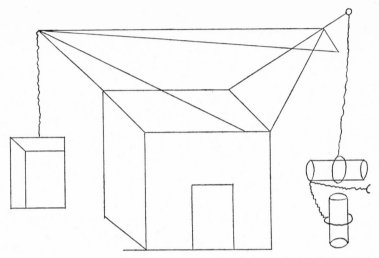

Fig. 43, the illustration for 3:10. The figure is taken from the MS L (3:4) and shows a column being shifted on its base by means of a lift built across a house or a wall, with a counterweight on the other side. See text p. 107 sq.

down upright on its base (or: in the right place on its base). And it is necessary to fasten the bottom of the column to its base so that it does not slip away from it when it is lifted or comes off it; or ropes are wound round the base of the column so that they become like a garland to it, so that when the column is lifted its lower end will be fixed in these ropes which are taken round it."

Carra de Vaux translates the first lines: "On a imaginé d'élever par le même moyen de grandes colonnes et de les asseoir sur les bases à l'endroit voulu. Dans ce système, on attache ..." Nix has: "Manche wollen nach diesem Verfahren auch grosse Säulen heben und auf ihre Postamente in einem beliebigen Orte niederlassen. Bei dieser Methode bindet man ..." Both seem to regard العمل "the method" as the same as الحيلة "the strategy"; but the latter corresponds to the Greek μηχανή, "contrivance", "engine". The sense is: Some people use the same method, that is, to balance a great burden with many small weights, and for this they use the following arrangement, that is, the ropes and pulleys and what not.

The special task here evidently is not to bring a column to its base, but to lift a column from its base just enough to shift it to its right position; this is clearly seen from the use of ropes for keeping the foot of the column in place during the lifting. The words: "The column comes down upright" probably translate ὀρθῶς, "rightly", "truly". This explains the فيبجلسوڢا where و would otherwise be to be expected; and this has led me to delete the و before بهذه الحيلة and to translate as I do.

Fig. 43 is taken from the Leiden MS. The house on which the crane is built is an already existing building, which is necessary for applying the method; no one would build "a solid tower" just for that. That the hanging column is not shown in an upright position I take to be an imperfection of the drawing. It is not possible to explain in detail the function of all the lines in the crane above the "tower", but the layout as a whole is quite clear.

"⟨11⟩ Some people want to move great burdens on the sea by this contrivance: They make a raft of square timber, whose single parts are kept together by nails and pegs, and provide it with strong sides, and place it in the water where they want to put on the burden; and they place under the raft sacks full of sand, with their mouths † tied, and they place the raft upon the sacks. Then they take two ships and lash them with ropes to the sides of the raft, on either side. Then they bring the burden on board the raft, and untie the sacks and let out the sand. Then they send out the ships on the sea, and they go over the sea carrying the raft.

[12] Some people also have found out to float the great stones on the sea in this way."

Carra de Vaux and Nix begin the next chapter, ch. 12, before the last sentence; but it seems to me that it belongs here rather than to the following text. Chapter numbers are not found in the MSS.

For the mouths of the sacks the MSS have two different words that give no sense; the conjectures by Carra de Vaux and Nix are not convincing. I cannot suggest something better; but the sense seem unmistakeable.

"⟨12⟩ Some people have contrived to set upright a wall that has become leaning by an earthquake, in this way." See fig. 44. "They dig in the ground on the side towards which the wall leans a trench as long as is the wall. Then they place in it a square piece of timber at a very small distance from the wall, and they place other timbers upright in what is between the wall and the square piece of timber that they have placed in the trench. Then they place on the ends of the upright timbers ⟨a cross timber, and tie to this cross timber⟩ pulleys, and pass through them the ropes to the engine called winch. Then they turn this engine so that the ropes are pulled and the cross timber is pulled and by its pulling the upright timbers are pulled and make the wall move until they bring it back to its position. And when they have brought it back into its position they leave it tied to this timber for some time so that the stones may come to rest upon each other. Then they untie the timbers, and the wall stands firm in its upright position."

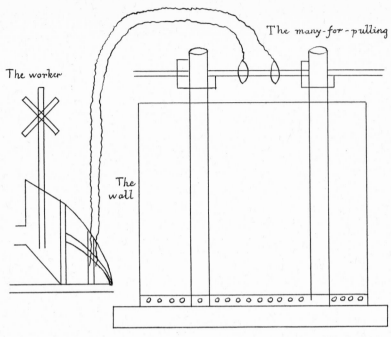

Fig. 44, the illustration for 3:12. The figure, which is taken from the MS L, (3:4), shows a wall being pulled upright by means of a capstan. This is called فاعل, "worker", which is certainly a translation of the Greek word ἐργάτης, which means either a workman or a capstan. This indicates that the drawing is originally Greek. See text p. 109 sq.

The cross-piece is mentioned later in the text and is shown in the figure, so it seems proper to put it into the place in the description where it belongs. With the many repetitions of the same words it is no wonder that it should have been left out.

Fig. 44 is taken from the Leiden MS. It shows quite clearly the beam at the foot of the wall, the uprights, the cross-beam, held by some sort of block, and two ropes leading to a capstan, which is shown in perspective. The circles at the foot of the wall I cannot explain.

Heron now has finished his remarks on transportation, and according to his promise in 3:1 he goes on to describe several presses. I have discussed this subject in my "Ancient Oil Mills and Presses" (14), to which the reader is referred for further details.

"⟨13⟩ As for what is necessary in the moving of the weights and what is of advantage in this, we have made good the explanation sufficiently; and now the

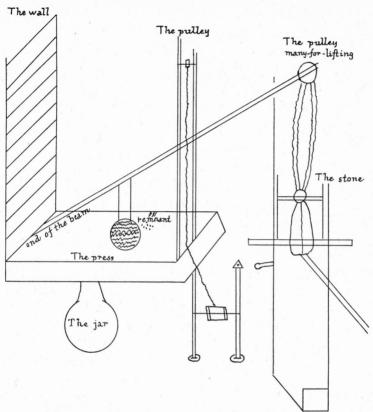

The wall

The pulley

The pulley
many-for-lifting

The stone

end of the beam

remnant

The press

The jar

Fig. 45a, the illustration for 3:13–14. The figure, which is taken from the MS L, (3:4), shows the press with the beam an the hanging stone. See text p. 110 sqq.

implements of agriculture, I mean the ones by which wine and oil are pressed, are not very different from what we have told about the use of the levers, and we have to make this clear and explain as much of it as is enough to know.

As for the beam that is called "mountain", which other people call a press-beam, it is nothing but a lever, and the stone that is placed under the lever, and that is the wall of the press-house into which the beam goes, and the weight, that is the rope wound round the crushed grapes, and the moving power is the stone that is hung from the beam, which is called *liṭus*. And it happens with the great beams that the stone is also great so as to be able to press. As for the long beam, its length may be five and twenty ells, and the stone hanging from it, which is called *liṭus*, its weight may be twenty talents."

See fig. 45a and 45b.

"The beam called 'mountain'". The Greek word ὄρον (n) or ὄρος

(m) means a press-beam; ὄρος (n) is a mountain. In 3:15 we read: "the beam that is called *aurus*", just as in 3:3 the implement that is called *audûs*", that is οὐδός, threshold. *litus* is λίθος, stone.

"The rope that is wound round the crushed grapes". The grapes were crushed first and yielded most of their juice before they were placed in the press. The mass might be pressed as it was, or contained in a *galeagra*, that is a wooden container, as described in 3:16, 17; or a rope could be wound round it to keep it in place. Carra de Vaux translates: "la corde enroulée autour du sac de plomb", which last must mean the mass to be pressed. Nix has: "das um die zu pressenden Trauben geschlungende Netz." The Arabic word حبل means a rope, and that is all that is necessary here. Carra de Vaux finds that the lever ought to pull the rope, since it represents the weight to be lifted, though he admits that it does nothing of the sort. In fact, Heron has left out of his description that the lever of the press works upside down: the hole in the wall, the fulcrum, keeps down the end of the lever; the lever presses down on the object of the levering, the pulp to be pressed, and the moving power, the stone, weighs down the lever.

The stone was a large weight that was hoisted up on the end of the press-beam and then left to itself; in this way the grapes were held under constant pressure for as long as was necessary, without further contribution of work on the part of the men.

The Greek ell was 46.24 cm; 25 ells then are 11.56 m. The twenty talents for the stone were 524 kg.

Fig. 45a is taken from the Leiden MS. It shows clearly the wall holding down the end of the beam; the press-floor; and the crushed grapes, with a rope wound round them, being pressed by a long beam. On its other end is a compound pulley which carries a stone. Connected with the press-floor is a container for the juice. So far it is very clear. The frame on the right, with the sloping lines, must represent the winch for lifting the stone; another winch, shown near the end of the press floor, would serve to lift the beam when the pulp had to be exchanged. The circles indicate that it is fixed in the ground.

In the interpretation of the inscriptions I differ twice from Nix, who has given not only Carra de Vaux's redraft of the figure, but also a true copy, as fig. 56a, p. XXXIV. Where he reads صـنـة (?) "Korb", I read صبّة "remnant"; where he reads معرضة (?) "Querbalken", I read معصرة "press" or, perhaps "press-floor".

"⟨14⟩ Now we want to arrange the hanging of the stone. So we use this method: We take an engine many-for-lifting and make a pulley fast to the end of the mountain and another pulley to the stone, and we make fast to the stone above the pulley a cross-piece which we hang on the beam that is called the mountain, and we pass this rope through to a drum on which there is a wheel, and we turn the wheel and the rope is wound round the drum and the stone is lifted."

Carra de Vaux takes this chapter to be profoundly corrupt; but since he has not understood the principle of the hanging stone at all, but insists both here and later that the stone must be fixed in the ground, his remarks are not very much to the point.

Nix takes the chapter as it is and explains the cross-piece fixed on the stone above the pulley as a means of lashing the stone to the press-beam, when it is left hanging.

This is corroborated by the figure in the British Museum MS, fig. 45b, showing a cross-bar sitting near the end of the press-beam, although no cross-bar is shown on the stone. We have, I think, to accept as a fact that when the stone was lifted as far as it could go, it was lashed to the beam by means of two cross-bars put in for the purpose, and that the winch was not used for holding it. This is also stated in 3:18: "when you have drawn up the stone and made it fast ..." When the stone came to rest on the ground, the compound pulley would have to be over-hauled, and then the stiffness of the rope might hamper the operation considerably.

But I cannot but feel that there is a lacuna in the text, because the rope that is mentioned right away after the cross-bar must be the rope from the pulley, not the rope for lashing. It would have to be something like this: "... and we make fast to the stone above the pulley a cross-piece ⟨and we take another crosspiece⟩ which we hang on the beam that is called the mountain ⟨and when the stone is lifted, we lash it to the mountain by means of these cross-bars; and the last pulley of the many-for-lifting should be sitting on the mountain⟩ and we pass this rope ..."

In a technical text like this it is always a moot question how many details it is necessary to explain; but Heron seems to aim at giving always the most complete instructions: "the beam ... comes down on the block, and the block is pressed, and the block presses on the board ... and the substance that is in the *galeagra* is pressed ..." So I cannot accept the text here as complete. Fig. 45b shows the same press as that shown in fig. 45a; it is taken from the British Museum MS. It is placed

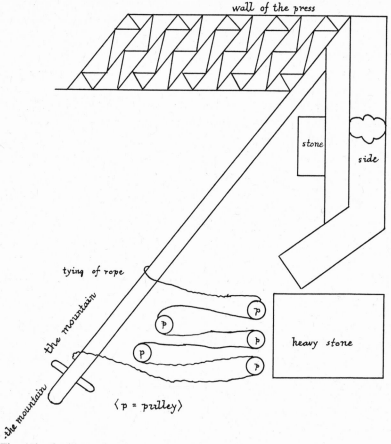

Fig. 45b, the illustration for 3:13–14. The figure, which is taken from the MS B, shows the press with the beam, the hanging stone, and the compound pulley. See text p. 112 sqq.

so that you have to turn the page 90° to get it right, but the letters follow those of the text, so that you get the figure wrong if you orient it by the letters. It is reversed compared with the Leiden figure, and very many of the details are lacking. In fig. 45c I have tried to show how the drawing of the press itself may have looked originally; it is difficult to recognize a wall in the queer criss-cross, but all the lines are there, only someone, an owner of an earlier MS (or his son?) has put diagonals across the ends of all the bricks. The jar of the Leiden MS is just indi-

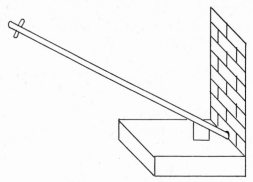

Fig. 45c, illustrating 3:13–14. This is my sketch to show how the wall, the press-bed and the beam may have looked originally in fig. 45b. See text p. 115.

cated. I cannot make anything but "side", جانب, out of the inscription where the Leiden figure has الجانّة, "the jar", written الحادس. The compound pulley is much more elaborate in the British Museum MS, and there is a cross-bar on the beam for lashing the stone. The text mentions only a cross-bar on the stone itself; that is not shown in either MS.

"⟨15⟩ We have also another engine by which we pull down the beam called *aurus* and lift the stone which is called *liṭus*. It is so that the stiffness of the rope causes some hindrance in pulling down the beam and in lifting the stone, because if the rope is stiff it will not run over the pulleys in the lifting the beam upwards and lowering the beam. And in lifting the stone we have to use long handspakes ⌈and the strong handspakes that are called in Greek *birunâ*⌉ with which to turn the winch; and we are not secure, if the crushed grapes that are under the beam are plenty, and those who turn this winch on which the rope is are many, against one of the handspakes breaking, and it falls down and they are hurt; or it slips out of the hole, and it falls down, and the same thing happens to them. So they have introduced another contrivance where no rope is needed, easier than that and more safe; and this is its description."

Nix has corrected "the beam" in the sentence "in lifting the beam upwards" into "the stone", which looks as if it was quite necessary. But all the MSS have "the beam", not "the stone", though in this way the beam comes into the sentence twice; and on reflection it is clear that the text is correct. The stiffness of the rope would matter very little, when the heavy stone was lifted; but when the beam had to be raised or lowered by means of the secondary winch, then the heavy rope would "cause some hindrance" by refusing to run over the idle pulleys. We must then take the first sentence "in pulling down the beam and in lifting the stone" as a general description, meaning just "the working of the press".

The words in ⌐ ⌐ are found in the MS B only, but it is easier to see how they can have been left out in the other MSS than to imagine how they can have come into B by themselves. For the Greek word, the MS has بزرا; Nix reads either بزرا, for πόρπη, or بزنا for περόνη. The two words mean the same thing, but since πόρπη is not found in Heron elsewhere, while περόνη is used quite often, I prefer to read بزنا, brnâ, for περόνη. This word means the tongue of a buckle, a buckle, a belay-ing-pin, a pivot, a linchpin, a rivet or bolt, p.p. Here we may take the first sense: the tongue of a buckle. These "strong spakes called buckle-tongues" I take to be short pieces of wood inserted in the holes for the handspakes to hold the drum, when the stone was being lashed to the beam.

"We use a square body of wood like a brick and make it fast beneath the beam that is called mountain in the place where the rope was fastened; and the part of it which is upwards is made round, and there is made on each side of the two sides of the place where it has to be fixed a tortoise fastened to the beam that is called mountain, so that this brick cannot move more than necessary, but is able to lean towards both sides. Then we lift the beam as high as it is lifted for the placing of grapes under it, and we measure the distance that is between the brick and the stone; and we take half of it, or a little more than that, and we make in this length a lentil-shaped screw of uniform thickness. And the screw furrow should not reach the end of the screw-stick at one end, but on the other end the screw-furrow must reach the end of the screw-stick. And we make the rest of the plank square, and we cut in this square a hole called *ṭurmus*, and that is round, drilled in the end of the block so that the block is joined to the wood which it has to be made fast to. Then we place this *ṭurmus* on one of the sides of the brick which is placed under the beam. Then we use iron cross-nails and fasten their ends in this furrow, and we nail the rest of them in the brick. And we also use an iron axle which we put into this *ṭurmus*, and we let it go to the brick and make it fast in it, so that it may increase the solidity and joint with the brick. Then we take another square, wooden block of hard, strong wood, of the same length as the screw; and its thickness, which is found from one of the sides, is a square whose base is longer than the diameter of the screw cylinder, so much as is needed for the placing of that cylinder inside this square wooden block. Then we split it into two halves lengthways, and we cut out in each of its two parts a furrow like a gutter, and round, in which we make a female screw; and we make in it a screw-furrow into which the male screw can be fitted. Then we glue together the two parts, so that they become one piece. Also in the female screw the screw-furrow must reach at one end to the outside of the block, but in the other end it is left without hole, solid. If we place the end of the screw into the end of the hollow block, where the screw-furrow reaches the end, and this is turned, the whole screw will go into the hollow block until it is hidden altogether. When we have done this, we cut out on the end of this inside hollow block a round furrow on its neck, a little way from its end, and fasten on it a ring of iron as we do on the wagon-axles. Then we cut out in the stone a hole into which the end of this block can be fitted, and the block should be able to turn in it easily. So we place the end of the block into the hole that is in the stone, and we make for it iron clamps, which keep the block from coming out of the hole that is in the stone; and we place in the round furrow that is in the end of the block also an iron ring, so that its turning becomes easy. And we make above this end that it fitted into the stone two holes at right angles to each other, from which the four ends of two handspakes come out. When we have done this and want to use the beam that is called the mountain, we bring together the ends of the screw and the hollow block. Then the four handspakes are turned and the beam is pressed down and the stone is lifted, and all that is under the beam is pressed. And when the stone is lowered so that it stands on the ground, we turn it in the opposite direction so that the beam is lifted, and the stone is standing firmly. And this method is effective, reliable, secure in its result, and without much fatigue."

It is unfortunate that there is no figure to help us here where the text for once is not very clear.

The general lay-out of the press presents no difficulties. In stead of the rope and drum, which could work only one way, we use a screw; the male screw is made fast to the press-beam, the female screw, which is as long as the male screw, is made fast to the stone, so that it can be turned. When we turn it one way, the female screw swallows the male screw, and the stone is lifted. Heron does not say that as soon as the stone leaves the ground, the stone turns, too, so that the friction between the screw-block and the stone ceases. When the pressing is done, and the stone has come down, we can lift the press-beam by turning the female screw the other way.

It is the fastening of the upper end of the screw to the press-beam that is not clear at all.

Carra de Vaux translates: "On emploie une pièce de bois équarrie, en forme d'oreiller[1] ([1]*Oreiller*, sens probable. Une autre lecture donnerait le sens de brique.), et on l'adjuste au-dessous du levier presseur appelé *chîl*, à l'endroit où se trouvait précédemment la corde. On la relie à un rouleau disposé au-dessus du levier presseur et l'on place sur celui-ci, de chaque côté du support fixe, des arrêts[2] ([2] *Arrêts*, sens probable, en cet endroit, du mot لكنانات, que nous avons rendu ailleurs par *tortue*. (Voir l. III, 1.)) destinés à restreindre la course de l'oreiller entre des limites convenables, tout en lui permettant de se déplacer dans les deux sens." I do not think that the text allows the interpretation "we tie it (the brick) to a roller placed above the press-beam". Nix has: "Wir benutzen einen viereckigen Körper von Holz, der wie ein Bachstein*) (*) gr. vielleicht πλινϑίov) aussieht, und befestigen ihn unter dem Oros genannten Balken an der Stelle, wo das Seil war. Den einen, nach oben gerichteten, seiner Teile machen wir rund, und auf beiden Seiten der festen Stütze bringen wir auf dem Oros genannten Balken fest-sitzende Hemmungen (?) an, damit dieser Backstein nicht weiter laufe, als nötig ist, sich aber doch nach beiden Seiten hin bewegen kann."

I think Nix is right in his description of the brick: it has to be placed under the beam, and its upper side has to be rounded. But neither Carra de Vaux nor Nix has explained the words الركن الثابت, which Carra de Vaux translates "le support fixe", Nix: "die feste Stütze". It cannot be the press-beam, for that is mentioned in the same sentence. We have met the expression before, in 3:2, where the guy-ropes for the one-mast crane are tied to اركان ثابتة; here it is a translation of μένοντα χωρία, "fixed places". So it may mean here the place where the brick has to be fixed, its staying-place.

Carra de Vaux's reconstruction, while not, I think, correct, is at least mechanically possible, which Nix's is not. The brick has to carry the screw, the block, and the stone; it is to be placed under the press-beam; so two "Hemmungen" would not serve to hold it. The Arabic word, as remarked by Carra de Vaux, translates the Greek χελώνη, which in 3:1 means a sled; but it means a lot of other things, all derived from the primary sense: a tortoise. If we seek for a sense to fit this place, I think we find it, not in χελώνη, but in the diminutive χελώνιov, which Vitruvius uses, in the plural *chelonia*, to describe two clamps on the two masts of a crane; they serve to hold the pivots of the drum. See further on p. 143. Since the brick has to be able to swing, that is, move just enought to let the screw keep its vertical position when the press-beam is raised and lowered, and since its upper surface is rounded, and itself is placed on the underside of the press-beam, it seems reason-able to expect that it was hanging from a pivot through a hole whose centre coïncided with that of the rounded part; and that this pivot was carried by two clamps fastened one at either side of the press-beam. This is a conjecture, but it takes in the elements found in the text. That the text is incomplete is evident, since it is impossible to reconstruct the joint from it with any certainty.

If we go on to the screw, we find that it is made of hard wood; there is a cylindrical part, in which the screw-furrow is made, right to its lower end; the upper part, where it has to be joined to the brick, is square. This end we have to pierce with a hole called *turmus*, which is the Greek word τόρμος; and this is explained as a round hole made in a piece of timber to fasten it to another piece of timber, that is a round hole for a wooden peg. Nix takes this to be a description of the joint here; I take it to be a general description of the *tormos*. Nix goes on: "Dann fügen wir diesen Tormos an die eine der unter dem Pressbalken gelegenen Seiten des Backsteins", where I translate: "Then we place this *tormos* on one of the sides of the brick that is placed under the beam." This must mean that the square head of the screw is placed against either the side of the brick that faces the press, or the side that faces the end of the beam, and that the hole is against the side. "Then we take cross-nails of iron and place their ends in this furrow and hammer the rest of them into the brick. And we use also an iron axle which we pass through this *tormos* and let it go to the brick and make it fast to it to increase the solidity and the joint with the brick." There are several difficulties in this: if an iron axle has to go through the hole, how can the iron cross-nails also be fitted into it? But if the "furrow" is not the *tormos*, what is it? The only certain thing is that the square end of the screw and the brick are fastened together with iron nails, and that next an iron axle is passed through the hole in the square end of the screw and made fast in the brick. Anyway, the text is quite incomprehensible to me, and probably defective. In 1932 I have tried to reconstruct the joint, taking for granted that the text was complete; but it has never seemed to me to be convincing. I shall now try to reconstruct it in another way, regarding the elements of the joint mentioned in the text as stray pieces of a jig-saw puzzle, and see whither this will lead us.

We may take it that the screw is not as thick as the press-beam; the brick then has to make up this difference. The brick probably was hung from a pivot placed in two clamps placed on the sides of the press-beam. Now the screw has to be fixed to the brick. The end of the screw is square and has a round hole throught it; we use iron cross-nails, whatever they are, and an iron axle going through the hole. It is tempting to suppose that this iron axle was the one to carry the whole joint: that it went through the tortoises, the brick and the *tormos*. This would mean that the brick had a deep cut to accomodate the square

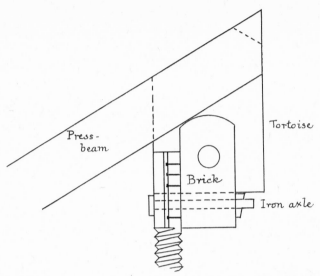

Fig. 46, illustrating 3:15. This is my own reconstruction of the joint between the head of the screw and the press-beam; I do not consider it as conclusive. See text p. 116 sqq.

end of the screw. This is a simple and pleasing solution, but it does not fit all the pieces. If the square of the screw was strong enough to carry the stone by an axle, there would be no need at all for the brick. Also it is said clearly that the square is placed against one of the sides of the brick, not that it is inserted in it; and it would be impossible to use nails from the square into the brick, if the square was sitting in a deep cutting inside the brick. We have to conclude that the function of the axle of iron was merely to join the square and the brick, and that the brick itself was hung from another axle from the two tortoises.

The square head then was placed against one side of the brick, either the one facing the press, or the one facing the outer end of the press-beam. The objection to this is that the screw is not hung symmetrically with regard to the pivot for the brick; but I cannot see how we can get round this with the text as it is. The iron axle going through the *tormos* must go through the brick also, and probably be provided with a head on one end and a wedge through the other. The cross-nails, whose ends are placed in a furrow, while their bodies are hammered into the brick, must have been right-angled hooks; their heads were placed in a furrow in the square end, because it was not solid

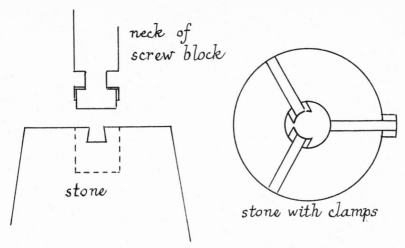

neck of screw block

stone

stone with clamps

Fig. 47, illustrating 3:15. This is my own reconstruction of the joint between the neck of the screw block and the stone; I take it to be fairly accurate. See text p. 121 sq.

enough to have nails going through it. They served to keep the head from turning on the axle.

This solution is consistent with the text as we have it, but it is not by any means certain.

In fig. 46 I have shown how this joint may have looked; one tortoise has been left out so that we can look inside the joint.

The preparation of the female screw is quite clear. It was not possible to make a screw inside a hole of this length, so the block has to be split and the furrows made in the two halves, which were then joined again.

The joint between the lower end of the female screw and the stone is also made quite plain: the block was turned cylindrical, a furrow was made into it; the end outside the furrow was reïnforced with an iron ring; and the side of the furrow that had to carry the stone with another iron ring. This ring cannot have been made in one piece, however. The neck goes into a hole in the stone, and the furrow with its ring is engaged by some sort of lock to keep it in while allowing it to turn. Nix translates the word ضبّ by "Haken" and shows a number of iron hooks driven into the stone and hooked over the ring. But in

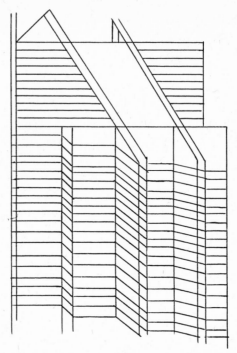

Fig. 48a, the illustration for 3:16. The figure is taken from the MS L and shows the composite *galeagra*. Cf. fig. 48b. See text p. 122 sqq.

3:19, see p. 128 sqq., the same word is used of the wooden fittings to hold the end of the screw of the direct screw press in the same way; see fig. 50a. Here they are doubtless boards sliding in a dove-tail groove and engaging the furrow in the end of the screw by a semicircular cut. So it seems reasonable to take these to be of the same shape. They would have the great advantage of being removable, which the nails are not. There is a slight disorder in the text, since the accusative is not marked: ܚܕܝܕ ܨܒܐܒ for ܚܕܝܕܐ ܨܒܐܒܐ. It is possible that ضباب was originally ضبّتين, two clamps. But there may have been three or more.

In fig. 47 I have tried to show how the joint was made. The clamps probably had either a hole or a knob to make it easier to drive them out, if it became necessary to take down the screw.

"⟨16⟩ Some people have contrived the construction of other sorts of implements for pressing; and they use, in stead of the rope that is wound round the stamped grapes, and in stead of the baskets in which the olives are placed after they have

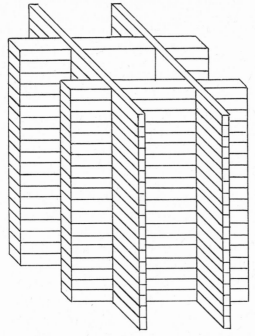

Fig. 48 b, illustrating 3:16. This figure is my attempt to show how the original for fig. 48 a may have looked. See text p. 124.

been crushed, and place under the mountain, an implement of wood which they call *galeagra*. They fill it with whatever they want and place it under the beam that they call the mountain and let the beam come down upon it. In this way they get at the same time plenty of room for what they want to press and ease in the work. This *galeagra* can be made of two kinds. One of them is built up, and it is made in this way: We take wood of a hard and firm nature and make of it planks of the same length as the implement we want to make, and a width of two spans, and their thickness should be six inches. Then we cut in both sides of both ends of each plank, having left standing six inches of it, a notch in its upper surface, and we go down into the substance of the plank one quarter of its thickness; and we do the same also on its underside, so that what is left will be one half of the thickness of the wood. And these notches made in the planks have to be uniform, so that they can be fitted into each other. Then we put together the planks so that when they all have been put together there is formed a square shape with equal sides like a chest. The gap in between the planks must be wide so that the juice can flow through it quickly. In this implement there is no need for the board on the grapes, and the laths that are put on over it, to be very thick, because when the grapes are pressed, as (the juice) is pressed out of them, the planks are taken away, so that they never get in the way."

The Greek word γαλεάγρα means a cage. The dimensions of the planks are: width two spans, that is two παλαίσται. The palaist was 77.1 mm; two of the ca. 15 cm. Thickness six inches, that is 6 daktyls. A daktyl was 19.3 mm; 6 daktyls ca. 11.5 cm. The planks were very nearly 6 by 4 inches English.

"The olives after they have been crushed." Nix follows the text and has: "nachdem sie mit einem Einschnitt (?) versehen worden." I suggest فدغ for فرض: "after they have been crushed."

The last part neither Carra de Vaux nor Nix has understood. Carra de Vaux translates: "Dans cet appareil, il n'est pas nécessaire que la pièce de bois placée sur la galéagre et les planches formant couvercle au-dessus d'elle, la ferment exactement, parce que, lorsque la pression s'excerce, il faut que les matières puissent remonter, sans quoi elles feraient obstacle au mouvement." Nix has: "Bei diesem Werkzeug braucht das Holtz, das auf den Trauben liegt, und die Platten, die dar-über aufgeschichtet werden, nicht sehr dick zu sein, weil sie, wenn die Trauben gepresst werden, (durch Auflegen neuer Platten) je nach dem Betrag des bereits davon Gepressten, über die Latten herausragen, sodass kein Hindernis aus diesen entsteht."

The pulp to be pressed was covered by a lid consisting of boards kept together by planks placed across them. This would fit the inside of the galeagra. When the press-beam came down, the planks of the galeagra could be taken away two and two, so that the galeagra was never in the way. This was the advantage of the built-up galeagra over the second galeagra with solid sides; here the lid had to form a block as thick as the galeagra was high. See p. 125 sq.

Fig. 48a is taken from the Leiden MS. The successive scribes have found the original perspective drawing too hard to copy. Another version is found in fig. 51a, showing the first galeagra in the second direct screw press.

In fig. 48b I have tried to show how the original of fig. 48a may have looked.

"⟨17⟩ As for the other *galeagra*, its four walls are joined to each other by three cross-planks on each of them; and it is necessary on these three cross-planks that there is something jutting out on the sides, cut by a cut half way through its thickness, so that it may be when they are put together, that the four walls are firmly joined. In this implement it is necessary also that the slits are broad; and there is placed on the upper board a block which sticks up, as we have already said, so that the beam shall not reach a part of the grapes †, but the block goes down to the bottom of the *galeagra*."

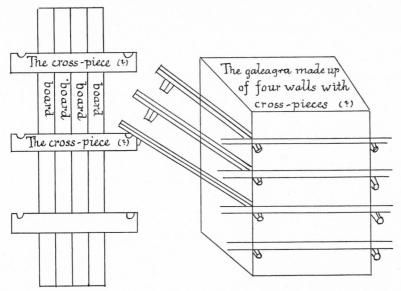

The cross-piece (?)

board board board board

The cross-piece (?)

The galeagra made up of four walls with cross-pieces (?)

Fig. 49, the illustration for 3:17. The figure, which is taken from the MS L, (3:4), represents the second, simple *galeagra*. See the text p. 124 sqq.

The description of the *galeagra* itself is quite clear. Nix has corrected "on these four cross-planks" into "on these three cross-planks", which is certainly correct, although in fact there were twelve cross-planks.

The last passage is not quite in order. Carra de Vaux has a slightly different text, which is not, however, noted in Nix's apparatus. He translates: "il faut placer sur un planche supérieur une espèce de chapeau[1] ([1]*Chapeau*, sens probable du mot قرمية), à une hauteur que l'on appréciera d'après ce que nous avons dit précédemment, afin d'éviter qu'une partie des matières ne remonte et ne projette ce chapeau en bas de la galéagre."

Nix has: "und auf die oberste Platte (muss) ein Stück Holz gelegt werden, das nach dem vorhin Erwähnten oben hinausragt, damit der Pressbalken nicht einen Teil der Trauben trifft, sondern der Holzklotz sich bis auf den Boden der Galeagra senkt."

In the first *galeagra* it was possible to take off the planks two and two as the press-beam came down; so a simple lid was enough. Here we need a block of wood to make up for the depth of the *galeagra*. The sentence: "so that the beam shall not reach a part of the grapes" gives no sense; it should be "so that the beam should not reach only a part of the grapes", which might be corrected by the addition of the word "only" فقط. But really it is not the beam, but the pressure that reaches the grapes, and the *galeagra* is the thing that the beam should not reach. I do not see how we can turn the words "some of the grapes" into "the galeagra". We might make it up like this: "so that the beam should not reach the *galeagra*, but still the pressure would not leave out part of the grapes, but the block goes down to the bottom of the galeagra." But all this is conjectural.

Fig. 49 is taken from the Leiden MS; it shows on the left one of the walls of the *galeagra*, four boards with three planks across, with notches in their ends. On the right we find the whole *galeagra* with four cross-planks in front and three on the left side. The joints at the ends of the planks are indicated not only on both ends of the planks in front, but also on these on the left, though there is no connexion with the planks that should go behind the *galeagra*. I cannot make out the words I have translated as "cross-planks" in the figure, but the sense is evident.

"⟨18⟩ Now we shall tell about the work with the presses with which you can press with force and power, and we tell the difference that is between the instruments we have described before and these instruments; and they are among the most powerful there is, and the most perfect. And first we shall tell the difference between the two sorts, and then we shall describe their making. And we say that the beam that is called the mountain is only a lever which a weight presses down, and the weight that presses it down is on its end that is lifted above the ground, and as long as it presses, the juices will not stop flowing until the weight sits on the ground. But in those instruments which we want to describe, they are very powerful, but their pressure is not also strong by continuation. And therefore it is necessary to repeat from time to time the turning and the pressure. But with the beam that is called mountain, when you have drawn up the stone and made it fast, then it presses all by itself, and there is no need to repeat the pressing several times. And this is the difference that is found between the two instruments."

The lever press with the hanging stone will exert its pressure all the time, since the beam comes down as the pulp shrinks; in the direct screw press the screw has to be turned now and then to renew the pressure.

"⟨19⟩ These instruments, whose construction we shall now describe, serve for the pressing of oil, and they are easy to work, they can be moved and put up in any place we want, and there is no need in them for a long, straight beam of a hard nature, nor for a very heavy stone, nor for strong ropes, and there is in them no hindrance from the stiffness of the ropes, but they are free from all that, and press with a strong pressure and the juices come out altogether. And their construction is what we now are going to describe.

We take a square piece of wood with a length of six spans and a width of not less than two feet and a thickness of not less than one foot; and the wood must be firm in its substance and not too green and not too dry, but in between, and we call it the table. We place this table flat, and we drill in both its ends at a short distance round holes deep into its substance, and we arrange for each hole two wooden clamps that go into the table, and their ends are hard (?), and they meet, and there is formed by them a small circle smaller than the round hole. The clamps should be cut on a slant, so that it will be, when they are fixed, that they stay and are not riven out at all. Then we get two strong planks, made straight and square by ruler, with the same thickness as width, and we let one head of each remain square for a suitable length, and we take off (?) the corners of the remaining part of the two planks and turn then round on their sides, and we cut in them a screw-line of equal thickness; and we place on the end of the screw-stick that we have left square a drum with four holes in it, and we put four handles into these holes. And the rest of the square is surrounded by a ring of thick wood, which is so far inside from its end as the depth of the round hole that we have drilled in the table ⟨...⟩ and the diameter of this circle should be half the diameter of the circle of the base of the screw. And when we have done this we fit the end of the screw in which there is this circular groove into the round hole that is in the table. Then we drive back the clamps which we have made till they go into the round groove and hold it fast, and the screw cannot get out. And we do the same with the screw that comes into the other end of the table. Then we take a square, long piece of wood of the same length as the lower plank into which the screws have been fitted, and there should be in this plank two round holes going into the substance of the plank and piercing to the other side, arranged as the round holes into which the ends of the screw go. And in these holes there should be made a screw furrow on the inside, so that they become female screws, so that it will be when the screws are turned the plank will be sent down, and in the same way also if they are turned the other way the plank is lifted. And as for how we make a female screw, this we are going to explain in the following. And the length and thickness of this plank has to be the same as we said about the size of the length and thickness of the table; but its width should be less than that width by a fourth of its width. Then we make for this table a square foot at right angles, which below looks like a step. And its length should be a little greater than the width of the table, so that the whole instrument can rest on it firmly. And we have to cut out the middle of the base with a suitable cut, and we cut the middle of the table with a cut corresponding to that cut which is in the base, and we fit one cut into the other so that it holds it in a very firm grip. Then we place on the table between the screws four walls put together of thin boards, whose thickness is less than an inch; and the length of this rectangle which is between those boards and its width should be of such a size that if the *galeagra* is set up inside it there will be between them a space surrounding the *galeagra*, in which the juice can flow. And we have to cut out in the middle of the table a groove corresponding to the surface of the *galeagra* where it touches the table, that is to say, it shall fit into it, and we place the *galeagra* into this groove. Then we place on top of it a thick board that fills out the *galeagra*, and we place upon it a block, less than the board in length and width, but so thick that it fills out the *galeagra*. Then we turn the screws by the handles that are on the wheels so that the beam with the female screw furrows in it comes down on the block, and the block is pressed, and the block presses on the board that is inside the *galeagra*, and the substance that is in the *galeagra* is pressed, and the juices run out. Then the screw is turned again the other way and the beam is lifted, and the block is taken off, and the pressed substance is shifted about until every bit of juices is pressed out."

No figure is given for this press in the Leiden MS, so we have to reconstruct it from the text; the description of the reconstruction will serve also for discussing the text in detail. See fig. 50a.

The dimensions of the table are: thickness one foot, width 2 feet, length six spans. The Greek foot, holding 16 daktyls, was 30.8 cm, which gives us a piece of timber 62×31 cm. In 3:16, see p. 122, the span was the palaist, of 4 daktyls, 7.7 cm long; six of them would be 46.2 cm, which is impossible as the length of a beam that is 62 cm broad. So, with Carra de Vaux, we must take *šibr* here to mean *spithamē*, of 12 daktyls; one *spithamē* was 23 cm, 6 of them, 72 daktyls, were 138.7 cm, which gives us a fair length for the table.

No dimensions for the screws are given. I have made them 6 daktyls or 11.6 cm square, and 7 feet, 112 daktyls, 216 cm long, including the part going into the table. I have placed the holes half a foot, 8 daktyls, 15.4 cm, from the ends, in the mid-line of the table. The clamps I figure as flat boards sliding in dove-tail grooves. Nix's half-circular boards held by wedges have no support in the text and do not look very likely.

The screw thread takes in only the upper half of the screw, since the beam cannot come down past the galeagra. The sticks have to be made round for the screw to be cut; the expression "we take the edges and turn them on the side" is queer, but it does not seem to me that Nix has bettered it by correcting بالنهي "on the side" into بالمبرد "with a file". It was quite possible to use a lathe at Heron's time. We now have a stick with a screw thread on half its length, while one end is left square. Then we place a wheel or drum on the square part, give it holes for handles, and put in the handles. There remains to make a furrow for the clamps. According to the text, which is followed by Carra de Vaux, the furrows for the clamps are made in the square part of the stick, which must have been rounded off so as to enter the hole

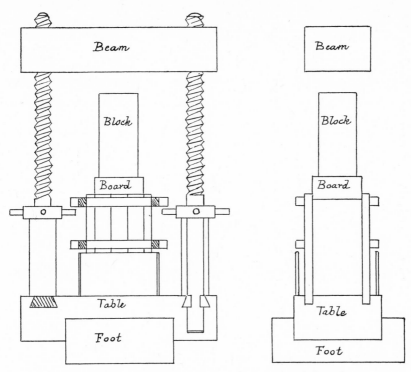

Fig. 50a, illustrating 3:19. This figure is my reconstruction of the twin screw press from the text. It is discussed in detail on p. 128 sqq.

in the table; and the rest of the square part, between the furrow and the wheel, is strengthened by a wooden cylinder placed round it. Carra de Vaux shows the wheel fixed almost at the bottom of the screw, which is threaded right down to the wheel, long past the galeagra shown in the middle. This is not convincing; there is no need to cut the screw where the beam cannot go, and it would be far more easy to work the handles if they were at a reasonable height above the ground. So I have placed the handles some 50 daktyls or about 1 m above the ground, just below the top of the galeagra. This explains the need for stiffening the screw-sticks that have to carry the weight of the beam when it is lifted. But for this interpretation it is necessary to assume a lacuna in the text, like this: "... the round hole that we have drilled in the table; ⟨and the rest of the square we make round, and make in it a furrow that can be fitted into the clamps that we put into the table⟩, and the diameter of this circle ...''

Nix, on the other hand, has placed the handles on the other end of the screws, above the press beam. But he has had to correct التربيع into العودين and بفرص into بعود, besides making two smaller, grammatical corrections, to make a text which is not very plausible after all. In 1932 I followed Nix; now I think that a lacuna is a better explanation here.

The press beam is like the table in length and thickness; it should be less broad by one quarter, that is 72 by 16 by 24 daktyls, or 140 by 30 by 40 cm. The four daktyls on either side are used for the galeagra. The screw-holes are made to correspond to the holes in the table; and if the square ends of the screw are downwards, the beam can be fitted over the screws right away. Otherwise it would be necessary to take out the clamps and put the screws through the beam from above. For this purpose the lower part of the screws must be of the same diameter as the core of the screw. In my drawing from 1932 (17) I made the mistake of making the rest of the screw-stick of the diameter of the screw; the beam could never have been fitted!

As for the foot to stabilize the press, both Carra de Vaux and Nix show it as both longer and broader than the table. I do not understand the text like that. The cut made into the middle of the foot and the cut made into the middle of the table have to be joined, which must mean that the foot is longer than the table is broad, and the table longer than the foot is broad. Besides, the part of the foot sticking out along the ends of the table would be in the way of the workers turning the handles. As for the remark that the lower part looks like a step, I take الدرج to be the Greek βάσις or βῆμα, which may mean either step or base; but I am not quite sure what it means.

Next we put up a wall, less than 20 mm thick, to keep in the juice; probably there must have been some outlet and a container, but nothing is said about it. Inside this wall we set up a *galeagra*. The first or composite *galeagra* cannot go on to this table at all, at least not with the dimensions given in 3:16. The table is 32 daktyls broad. From the length of each plank of the galeagra go four times its thickness: 6 daktyls at either end for the cut, and 6 daktyls outside the cut, that is 24 daktyls, leaving only 8 daktyls, or 15 cm, for the inside width. If we take the width of the press-beam to correspond to the inside of the simple *galeagra*, we have four daktyls on either side: one daktyl or less for the wall;

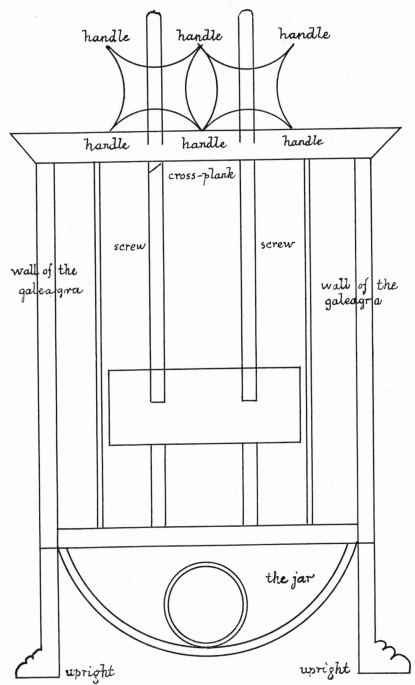

Fig. 50b, the illustration for 3:19. The figure is taken from the MS B and shows a twin-screw press; but it is not compatible with the text at all. See the text p. 132.

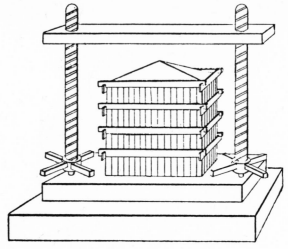

Fig. 50c. Carra de Vaux's figure of the twin screw press, 3:19. See text p. 132-133.

one daktyl or less for the canal for the juice; two daktyls and at most one half for the *galeagra*. Since the *galeagra* is fitted into the table, we can leave out the lowest of the three sets of locking cross-planks; the next one could be above the wall.

We now need only a lid for the pulp and a block to follow the lid down where the press-beam cannot go.

To make this press and the next it is necessary to be able to cut a female screw into a thick plank; Heron promises us to tell how this is done, and describes it in ch. 21. The importance of this remark for the chronology of the press will be discussed on p. 140.

The Leiden MS, as I have said, has no figure to illustrate this chapter; fig. 50a is my reconstruction, built upon the text. But the London MS, B, has a figure, shown here as fig. 50b, and it is this figure that has inspired Nix to make his reconstruction, shown here in fig. 50d, while fig. 50c shows Carra de Vaux's figure.

The MS figure takes up a whole page after the end of the book; it shows unquestionably a twin screw press with the handles at the upper end of the screw, and so far gives support to Nix's reconstruction and to his corrections in the text. On the other hand, it has so many features that are incompatible with the text, that it seems impossible to accept it as belonging with the text as we have it. The table is not "placed flat", if that means that it is placed on the ground, and it is not supported

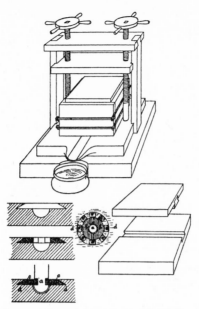

Fig. 50d. Nix's figure of the twin screw press, 3:19. See text p. 132-133.

by a foot "looking like a step", and fitted into a cut; here the table is part of a frame consisting of two uprights with a cross-beam at their upper ends. The two screws go through this beam, presumably in smooth holes, and carry a press-beam or rather a lid that is only five eighths of the table in length. Outside this, inside the uprights, the thin wall of the galeagra is seen, reaching from the table to the fixed cross-beam above. The press-beam then goes down into the galeagra, and so do the screws, so that they have to be standing in the pulp. There is also shown what I take to be an extension of the table, in its whole length, formed like a segment of a circle, with a container to take the juice.

We have either to assume that a whole chapter, describing this variant of the twin screw press, has vanished altogether, or that this drawing is a later addition, a drawing of an actual press with no relation to the text itself.

"⟨20⟩ There is also another implement with a single screw, and that is so that we make on the table two uprights that carry the cross-beam in which there is the female screw-hole; and the screw-hole should be in the middle of the beam. Then the screw is put into this hole, and it is turned by the handles that are on the wheel, so that the screw comes down on the board that is fitted into the *gale-*

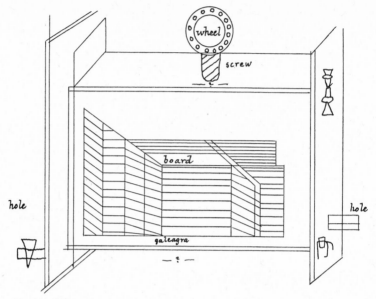

Fig. 51 a, the illustration for 3:20. The figure is taken from the MS L and shows a single-screw press with the composite *galeagra*. Fig. 51 b is an attempt to reconstruct the original figure. See text p. 134 sq.

agra; and it presses it, and the juices run. And we have to repeat the pressing again and again till no more juices are left in the pressed substance.

And there are many other kinds of presses than these, which we do not choose to describe, because they have been in use in great numbers for a long time among the common people, although they are not as effective as those that we have described."

Fig. 51 a is taken from the Leiden MS; it shows the single screw press with the first *galeagra*. The figure is not quite so confused as it may appear at first sight. The *galeagra*, even though less well conserved than the one in fig. 48 a, is easy to recognize; and the two upright sides, the two horizontal planks, and the single screw in the middle are not difficult to perceive, if we begin from the right hand side of the drawing. The left hand side is less successful; but if we remove the false top on the upper plank, and move the vertical double line from the fore-edges of the two horizontal planks to the back, behind the galeagra, we need only a horizontal line for the back of the bottom to have an almost complete figure. See my sketch fig. 51 b.

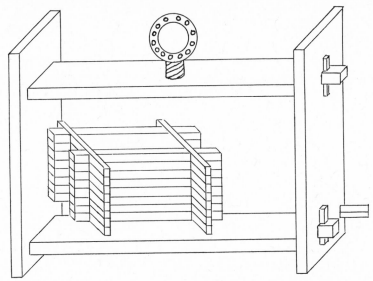

Fig. 51 b, illustrating fig. 51 a. This is my interpretation of the MS figure, fig. 51 a.
It is discussed in the text p. 134 sq.

It seems quite evident that the sides were broader than the horizontal
planks, and that they went below them and above them; the joints were
made by tenons and wedges. The square marked "hole" on the right
hand side I take to be an outlet for the juice; another outlet on the other
side is hidden by the side, but the inscription shows where it would
come. The thing below the word "hole" I take to be a tenon with a
wedge.

The inscription just below the screw, فصد or فصل, and the one under
the press-bed المِلبره or المِلسة, I cannot make out.

Fig. 51 b is an interpretation of fig. 51 a. Since the press is certainly
axonometrical towards the right, and the *galeagra* just as evidently
axonometrical towards the left, it is not possible to make them fit each
other. This I think is why the left side of the press has got out of hand.
When I consider the difficulty of getting a complicated figure like that
of the composite *galeagra* right, I find it quite a wonder how good the
MS figures are after all.

"⟨21⟩ As for the female screw, it is made in this way: we take a piece of hard
wood, whose length is more than twice the length of the female screw, and its thickness like that of the female screw, and we make on one part on half the length of the

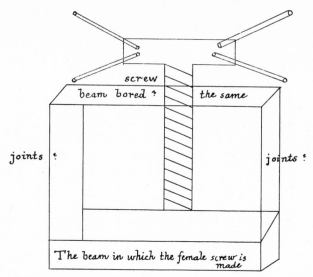

Fig. 52a, the illustration for 3:21. The figure, which is taken from the MS L, shows the screw-cutter making a female screw. See text p. 135 sqq.

piece of wood a screw in the way we have already described, and the depth of the screw-turns on it should be like the depth of the screw-turns which we want to turn in this female screw. And we turn from the other part as much as the thickness of the screw-turns, so that it becomes like a peg of equal thickness. And we draw two diameters on the base of the piece of wood, and we divide each of them into three equal parts. And we draw from one of the two points a line at right angles to the diameter. Then we draw from the two ends of this line at right angles to this diameter, on the whole length of the peg, two lines at right angles; and this is easy for us to do, if we place this peg along a straight board and scratch it with the scribe (?) until we reach the screw-furrow. Then we use with great care a fine saw, till we have sawed down to the screw-furrow; then we cut off this third that was marked on the peg. And we cut out in the remaining two thirds, in their middle, a groove like a canal on the whole length, and its size should be half the thickness of the remaining part. Then we take an iron rod and sharpen it according to the screw-turnings; then we fit it into the peg with the canal in it. Then we make its end come out into the screw-turns, after we have fastened the two pieces together with a strong fastening, so that the two are fixed to one another and cannot come apart at all. Then we take a small wedge and insert it into the canal-like groove and knock it until the iron rod comes out and lies between the two parts. When we have done this, we fit the screw into a piece of wood into which there has been bored a hole that corresponds exactly to the thickness of the screw. Then we bore in the sides of this wide hole small holes side by side, and we fit into them small, oblique, round pegs and drive

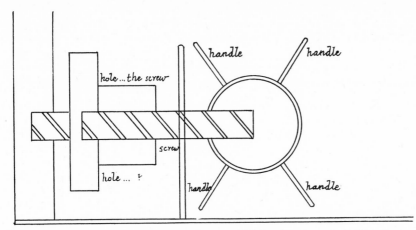

Fig. 52b, the illustration for 3:21. The figure, which is taken from the MS B, shows the screw-cutter making a female screw. See text p. 135 sqq.

them in until they engage the screw-furrow. Then we take the plank in which we want to make the female screw, and we bore in it a hole of the size of the screw-peg; and we make a joint between this plank and the plank into which we have fitted the screw by strong cross-pieces, which we fasten very solidly. Then we insert the peg that carries the wedge into the hole that is in the plank in which we want to cut the female screw, and we bore on the upper end of the screw holes in which we place handles. And we turn it till it comes into the plank, and we keep on turning it up and down, and we serve the wedge with blows again and again, until we have cut out the female screw with the furrow we wanted. And so we have made the female screw. And this is the figure, and with it ends the book."

The figure with which the book ends is shown here in two versions; in fig. 52a from the Leiden MS, in fig. 52b from the one in the British Museum.

The Leiden figure shows the screw going through two planks held together by cross-pieces at the sides. The screw carries a wheel with four handles, where the text mentions only holes through the stick itself. The inscriptions on the upper plank and on the sides are doubtful.

The second figure is poorer still, and the inscriptions, apart from the word "screw", are rather illegible.

Neither figure gives us the slightest idea of the details of the screw-cutter as described in the text; so we have to reconstruct it mostly from the text itself.

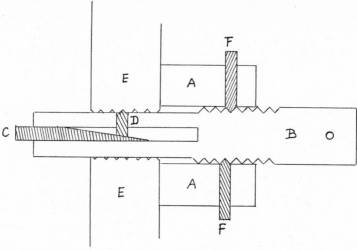

Fig. 53a, illustrating ch. 3:21. This is a cross-section of my reconstruction of the screw-cutter. AA is a block with a smooth hole to take the screw-stick, B, that carries the boring-bar with the canal. C is the wedge that drives out the cutter D; EE is the plank to be cut, and FF the pegs to engage the guiding screw. See text p. 135 sqq.

It works like this: to make a screw-thread inside a hole we either have to split the block, as in ch. 3:15, or we have to cut or scratch the furrow with a cutter guided by a screw of the same shape as the one for which the female screw is made, and at least as long as the female screw. For guiding this screw we need a female screw, but since we cannot make it yet, we use a makeshift: the screw goes into a smooth hole, but its furrow is engaged by small pegs coming in through holes in the block.

The other end of the screw-stick is turned to the thickness of the core of the screw, so that it fits into the hole for the female screw. The cutter is carried by this boring-bar; but it cannot cut the furrow to its full depth at once, so it has to come out little by little, and this is effected by a wedge operated from the end of the boring-bar. Since the guiding screw cannot enter the female screw till it is finished, the cutter has to sit in the boring-bar as far from the screw as the plank to be bored is thick; and the boring-bar must be so much longer that the wedge has a proper backing. The other end of the screw-stick has to have handles for turning, so that the whole screw-stick will be more than twice as long as the female screw.

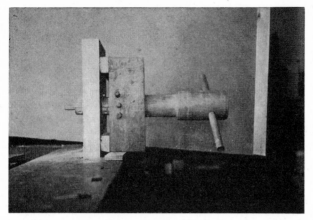

Fig. 53b. Photograph of my model of Heron's screw-cutter
in action. Compare fig. 53a.

In fig. 53a I have shown the implement in a cross section. AA is
the block with the smooth hole; B is the screw-stick. It has a hole for
a handle and a screw-thread, and it ends in the boring-bar with the
canal for the wedge, C, that drives out the cutter D. EE is the plank in
which the female screw is beginning to appear, and FF two pegs to
engage the leading screw. The cross-pieces to keep together AA and
EE are not shown, as they have to sit on the sides where the pegs FF
are not.

When I first published my interpretation of the text in 1932, a
reviewer declared that it was "mechanically impossible". To settle this
question I made a life-size model of the implement and found that it
worked quite well. The experiment is described in the Journal of Hellenic Studies (18). Fig. 53b shows a photograph of the screw-cutter in
action.

The description now should be quite easy to understand, except
where the text is at fault. The text has: "we draw two diameters of the
two bases", which Nix corrects into: "a diameter of the base", and
later "and divide each one of them" into "and divide it". The dualis
"two bases" is obviously wrong, but the two diameters are right, for
we need both diameters and all four dividing points; the first for the
segment to be cut off and for the bottom of the canal; the second for
the two sides of the canal. See fig. 54.

For "the scribe" Nix has "mit einer Zange". The MSS have بالكاسكر

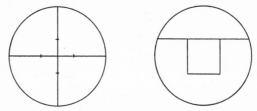

Fig. 54, illustrating ch. 3:21. The figure shows the marking of the flat end of the boring-bar. On the left the two diameters are divided each into three equal parts; on the right the marks are used for the segment to be cut off, and for the canal. See the text p. 139.

بالمَكَايس, and بالكَايس, all of which is without meaning; Nix reads بالكلبتين "with a forceps". He translates the whole sentence: "Dies erreichen wir, wenn wir den Pflock auf eine gerade Platte legen, und ihn mit einer Zange furchen." But it is quite easy to scribe a line along a cylinder, if we place it, not on, but alongside a straight board of approximately half the thickness of the cylinder. Since none of the MSS shows an Arabic word, I suggest that the Greek word, ἀκίς, "a point", written بالاكيس, is meant.

"We take an iron rod and sharpen it according to the screw-turnings." The text has "and turn it", which gives no sense. I suggest فنحدّه for فندير.

From the fact that Heron describes the female screw made in a split block (3:15), and then goes on to describe the direct screw press with a female screw cut into the solid beam, adding, as if to re-assure us, that he is going to tell us how it is done, I conclude that the screw-cutter at this time was something new; and I think it quite probable that it was invented by Heron himself. That it does belong to this time is seen also from a remark by Plinius (99), who wrote about 75 A.D. that within the last 22 years people have begun to use direct screw presses and *galeagras*. See my work from 1932 (15).

Vitruvius

Vitruvius wrote his work "On Architecture" in 25 B.C. (129); it consists of
ten books, of which the tenth and last deals with engines of many sorts,
which are used by architects. A reliable insight in the construction and
use of the engines is necessary for planning a piece of work and computing the costs, he says; that is why he has to write about them.

No figures are found in the MSS; but in two places at least he refers
to a figure placed on the back of the roll, but this figure now is lost.
The figures given here have been drawn by myself according to my
interpretation of the text.

"10:1. A machine is a coherent material structure with very great powers for
moving burdens. They are moved by the art of the turning of circles, which the
Greek call κυκλικην κινησιν. But there is a sort of climbing apparatus, which
in Greek is called ακροβατικον; another moved by wind, which among them
is called πνευματικον, and a third for pulling, and this the Greek call βαρουλκον.
The climbing apparatus is when the machines are so set up, that you can climb
high up without danger by upright poles and cross-pieces lashed to them; that
moved by wind, however, when wind driven by forces and strokes and voices
are expressed οργανικως; for pulling, on the other hand, when burdens are
drawn by engines so that they are lifted high up and placed there. The climbing
way does not pride itself on ingenuity but on daring; they consist of joints and
cross-pieces and plaited lashings and props of buttresses. But that which takes
on entrances by the power of wind aims at the fine effects of art by ingenuities.
The pulling, however, has possibilities for usefulness greater and full of splendour,
and great advantages in working with prudence. Among these some work
μηχανικως, others move οργανικως. Between engines and organs there seems
to be this difference, that the engines are forced to have effect by several operations and greater force, as the catapults and the press-beams of the presses; while
the organs do their work by the safe touch of a single operation, as the turnings
of the scorpions or the differential gears. So both organs and the way of engines
are necessary for use, and without them no thing can be but hampered. But
every machinery is made according to the nature of things, with the turning of
the universe as teacher and instructor. For let us remark the First Thing and
let us regard that which contains the nature of the sun, the moon, also the five
stars * * * * they turn by machinery, we would not meanwhile have had light
and the ripenings of fruits. So when the ancients had found that these things were
like that, they took patterns from the nature of things and by imitating them
led by the divine things they made apt implements for our life. Thus they obtained,
so that they might be more handy, some things by engines and their turnings,
a few things by organs, and thus what they saw to be useful for use by study,
art, teaching, they took care to increase gradually by doctrines. For let us remark

something invented first because of need, like clothing, how in the organic use of the fabrics the combination of the warp with the weft not only protects the body by covering it, but also adds the beauty of ornament. Nor would there have been plenty of food, if yokes and ploughs had not been invented for the oxen and all draft animals. If drums and press-beams and handspakes had not been procured for the presses, we could not have had the sheen of oil or the fruit of the vine for our pleasure, nor could they have been transported, unless contrivances had been found for drays or carts on land, and for ships on the sea. The invention of the examination by balances and scales with weights saves our life from iniquity for honest ways. There are also countless ways of constructions of implements about which there seems to be no need to write, because they are not ⟨unknown, but⟩ at hand daily, like the mills, the bellows of the smiths, wagons, gigs, lathes, and other things, that have common opportunities for use by custom."

This is the first chapter of the tenth Book, and I think that the reader will feel how different the atmosphere is from that of Heron.

Still, though the expression is awkward, there is good sense in this chapter. All mechanical contrivances are referred to the turning of circles, as in Aristoteles and Heron. The implements are divided into climbing apparatus, that is scaffolding; pneumatic apparatus, like pumps and water-organs; and cranes and hoists.

Next he divides the engines proper into mechanisms and organs; by mechanisms he seems to mean engines compounded of different kinds of powers, like the catapults, where the compound pulley is used for drawing back the arms that project the missile, or the wine-press, where the winch pulls on the beam working as a lever. An organ then ought to be a simple engine, which holds good of the differential gear (see p. 146 sq.), but hardly fits the scorpion, which is just a small catapult.

Anyway, the pattern of all engines is the construction of the heavens, where the stars in their courses follow circles, as he has described it in Book 9. This has been explained further in the lacuna, which I cannot undertake to fill out.

Some examples of inventions and their great usefulness end the chapter.

This theoretical and teleological introduction was necessary, it seems; now he has got through it, he can get down to his real task, the description of the engines. Here he is at home; you feel in every word of the rather long-winded explanations that he has worked with the cranes himself many a time.

"10:2. So let us begin to explain about the things that seldom come to hand, that they may be known. And first we shall teach about those that must be pro-

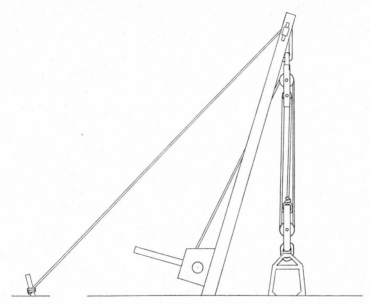

Fig. 55a is a sketch of the crane described by Vitruvius 10:2:1–2, seen from the side.
See text p. 142 sqq.

cured for sacred buildings and towards the perfection of public works. They are made like this: Two posts are procured with due regard to the size of the burdens. They are set up sloping from the heads, that are held by a clamp, outwards towards the lower part; they are held upright by ropes tied to their tops and arranged round about. In the top is made fast a block, which some call *rechamus*. In the block are placed two pulleys turning on axles. Over the ⟨upper⟩ pulley the hauling rope is passed, then it is let down and is passed over the pulley in the lower block. Then it is brought back to the lower pulley in the upper block, and so it comes down to the lower one and is tied into its hole. The other end of the rope is led to the lower part of the implement. 2. On the square backsides of the poles, where they come apart, tortoises are fixed, into which are placed the ends of drums, so that the axles turn easily. Such drums have near either head two holes so arranged that handspakes may be inserted in them. But to the lower block iron tongs are lashed, whose teeth are placed in the stones provided with holes. Now when the rope has its end tied to the drum and the drawing handspakes turn it, the rope is drawn tight by winding ⟨itself⟩ round the drum, and so it lifts the burdens to a height and the placings of the works. 3. Now this sort of engine is called *trispastos* because it goes round three pulleys. But if two pulleys turn in the lower block, three in the upper, it is called *pentaspaston*. But if engines are to be procured for greater burdens, greater lengths and thicknesses in the posts must be used, ⟨and⟩ in the same proportions the arrangements are

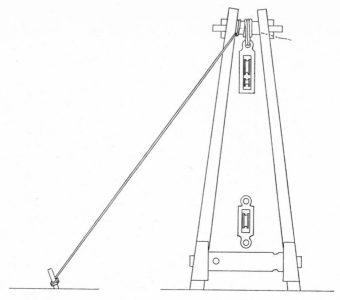

Fig. 55b is the same crane as in fig. 55a, seen from behind. See text p. 142 sqq.

made in the top for the cross-pieces, below for the turnings of the drums. When this is brought about, the ropes for erecting, hitherto loose, are made fast, and the stays over the shoulders of the engine are distributed to points far away, and if there are no places where they can be tied, posts leaning backwards are dug down and made fast by stamping round them, to which the ropes are tied. 4. A block is made fast on the top of the engine with a strong rope, and from it a rope is led to a post and put through a block tied to the post. The rope is made to go round its pulley and led back to the block that is tied to the head of the engine. The part of the rope that comes round the pulley comes down from the top and goes to the drum that is at the foot of the engine, where it is made fast. When the drum turns, forced by the handspakes, it sets up the engine by itself without danger. Then the engine is held upright by ropes and stays fastened to posts round it to a greater extent. The blocks and the hauling ropes are arranged as described above."

The first four verses of chapter 2 consist of two parts: first a description of a crane, next instructions on how to set up a crane heavier than usual.

The crane is shown in fig. 55a and b in a reconstruction made from the text; the description is so clear that there is hardly any room for doubt.

The word *rechamus* is explained by Georges (41) as *trochlea superior,*

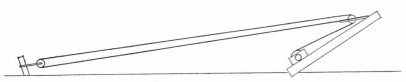

Fig. 56 is a diagram of the setting up of a heavy crane as described by Vitruvius 10:2:3–4. See text p. 143 sqq.

"der erste Kloben", that is, "the first block". But later in our text, where the tongs are tied to the lower block, the word *rechamus* is used again, so it means just a block and no more.

There is only one drum. The plural is used for a general description of the winch: the tortoises are gadgets into which drums are placed; the drums have four holes. But when the rope comes down, it is fixed to the drum, singular.

For the tongs I have drawn one of Heron's "crabs", see p. 104 sq; but "the tongs that go into holes in the stones" might also have been his hanger, see p. 105 sq.

The experience of the author is shown by the handling of the rope. One end of the rope is led through the two blocks and tied home on the lower block; the other end goes to the drum. It would be possible to tie the end to the block first and then take the rope through the blocks and lead it to the drum; but the other way is best, because it makes it possible to exchange the triple pulley for a five-way pulley, for instance, without taking the rope off the drum.

For the ordinary Roman house of one story no cranes were used; they had to be procured for temples and public buildings of greater height.

Fig. 56 is a diagram of the setting up of a heavy crane by means of its own winch. The operation is only possible when the head of the crane is lifted some way above the ground, say as far as the men could lift it easily. Before lifting it the rest of the way, we have to tie the stays to its top and distribute them to the points where they have to be tied; where necessary, we put up strong "fixed places", as Pappos has it (see p. 98): posts, not vertical, but sloping away from the crane, to hold the stays. Then, when the big thing has come up, we are ready to secure it. Let us notice here also the care for the men: the operation must be without danger.

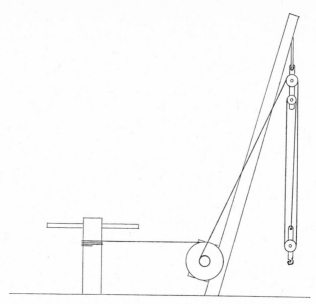

Fig. 57 is a diagram of the crane with a differential gear, described by Vitruvius 10:2:5–7. Cf. the trispastos in Oreibasios, fig. 67a. See text p. 146 sq.

"10:2:5. But if burdens more colossal in bulks and weights are in the workings, it cannot be trusted to a drum, but just as the drum is held by the tortoises, so an axle is put in with a large disc in the middle, which some people call a wheel, but the Greek αμφηρην, others περιθηκιον. 6. But in these engines the blocks are not arranged in the same way, but otherwise. For they have both below and above a double set of sheaves. The drawing rope is passed through the hole in the lower block in such a way that the two lengths of the rope are equal, when it is stretched out; and here, by the lower block, both parts of the rope are held by a thin cord wound round and made fast, so that they cannot go either ⟨to the right or⟩ to the left side. Then the ends of rope are led to the upper block from the outside and passed over the lower sheaves, and they go back down and are passed from the inside round the sheaves of the lower block, and they are taken back to the right and the left ⟨and⟩ come to the head round the upper sheaves. 7. They are passed through from the outside and go down right and left of the disc in the axle, and are tied there, so that they hold. Then, however, another rope is wound round the disc and is led to a capstan, and when this is turned, ⟨it turns⟩ the disc and the axle, ⟨and the two ropes⟩ are stretched equally by being wound round it, and so they lift the burden softly without danger. But if a greater wheel is placed either in the middle or in one of the outer ends, it may have a swifter effect on the work without a capstan, by treading men."

Fig. 57 is a diagram of the construction. The ropes from the blocks go round the axle, the rope from the capstan round the disc. This is the differential gear mentioned 10:1:3 as *anisocyclorum versationes*, "the turnings of the unequal circles", and the one used by Heron, 2:21, in stead of gear-wheels, see p. 83 sq., and by Oreibasios, see p. 178 sqq.

For very heavy burdens a double rope and double tackleblocks are used; this also allows of a symmetrical arrangement of the ropes on either side of the disc. Since the two parts of the rope must carry exactly half of the burden, the middle of the rope is made fast first to the lower block, and the two ends passed through the blocks and fastened to the axle. It would probably be expedient to tighten the rope just enough to let the middle settle in the ring of the lower block before lashing it.

The greater wheel and the treading men that do away with the capstan are to be seen on two reliefs (10, 37, 70, 74); the men are working inside the wheel like squirrels in a cage.

"10:2:8. There is, however, another sort of engine, quite clever and contrived for working with speed, but only experts can make use of it. It consists of a beam that is set up and held by stays in four directions. Under the stay two tortoises are fixed, a block is fixed by ropes over the tortoises, under the block is placed a stick about two feet long, six digits broad and four thick ($60 \times 11 \times 7$ cm). Blocks are placed having three sets of three sheaves side by side. So three hauling ropes are tied on ⟨the top of⟩ the engine. Then they are led to the lower block and are passed from the inside through its upper sheaves. Then they are led to the upper block and are passed from the outside to the inside over the lower sheaves. 9. When they have come down to the lower block, they are passed from the inner side and over the second sheaves to the outer side and are led to the top towards the second sheaves; having passed through, they go down, and from below they are led to the head; having passed over the upper sheaves, they come down to the foot of the engine. But at the root of the engine there is placed a third block; this the Greek call επαγοντα, but we *artemo*. This block is tied to [the block of] the root, and it has three sheaves, over which the ropes are passed and are then given to men to haul. Thus three gangs of men pulling without a capstan swiftly lift the burden to the top. 10. This sort of engine is called *polyspaston*, because it yealds the highest ease and swiftness by many turnings of sheaves. The single set up of the beam has this advantage, that by leaning it can put down the burden before it as far as it likes and to the right and left side."

The general lay-out of this crane is quite clear, but some of the details are puzzling. Since there is only one mast, it has to have tortoises on it, that is, clamps for fastening a rope on the top. But why is a block placed on the rope to carry the cross-plank? And why a cross-plank at all, since there is only one block of nine sheaves up above? The singular is used both for the upper and for the lower block, when the instructions for the ropes are given.

It may be worth noting that the triple block at the foot of the mast is also tied to a block. The editor deletes these words, but is he right? It is possible that the crane-mast is meant for ordinary work, and that Vitruvius tells us how to rig it for this special use. The single mast cannot carry a winch, so it has to have a "third block" at the foot for leading the rope to a capstan. If we want to use it for three gangs, we put in one block of nine sheaves at the top, tying it to the block already there; a similar block is used for the burden, and a block of three sheaves side by side is tied to the single block at the foot of the mast. The cross-piece may be meant to take the ends of the three ropes. The text says that they are "tied to the engine". The editor fills out the lacuna "to the top of the engine". But it may have been "to the cross-plank on the top of the engine". Another possibility is that the text is incomplete, and the cross-plank is meant to take three ordinary three-sheave blocks, if we do not possess a block of nine sheaves. But there is no irregularity of the text here to support this supposition.

"10:2:10 (cont.) The workings of all the engines described above are prepared not only for these things, but also for loading and unloading ships, some of them being upright, others horizontal, placed in fittings that turn. Likewise also without settings up of beams the haulings of ships are performed on level ground in the same way and by an arrangement of ropes and blocks."

Vitruvius now has done with the cranes and goes on to tell a few anecdotes of special tasks performed by special methods.

"10:2:11. It is not amiss also to explain the clever way of Chersiphron. When he wanted to transport the shafts of the columns from the quarry to the temple of Dian in Ephesus, he did not trust wagons, because of the greatness of the burdens and the rural softness of the roads, and so that the wheels should not be swallowed, he tried this way. Out of timber of four digits (7.4 cm) he constructed four shafts * * * * with two cross pieces between, of the same length as the shafts (of the columns) and joined it and fastened with lead into the ends of the shafts iron pivots like swallow-tails, and put bearings into the wood to contain the pivots; but the pivots sitting in the bearings turned easily. Now when oxen hitched to them drew them along, the shafts turning on the pivots and the bearings rolled along the ground without stopping."

In spite of the lacuna the text is quite easy to understand: Chersiphron put pivots into the ends of the shafts and rolled them along the soft ground like enormous garden rollers. The frame consisted of two beams behind, two in front, and two cross-beams that carried the bearings. The word *subscus* means a double dove-tail or a figure like an hourglass. This is the shape of the foot of the pivot, where it is made fast to the stone; this construction is known from mill-stones for water-mills (83, 104); cf. p. 152, 203.

> "10:2:12. But when they had transported all the shafts like that, and the transports of the epistyles became pressing, Metagenes, the son of Chersiphron, rearranged the transport of the shafts also for the conveyance of the epistyles. He made wheels of about twelve feet (3.5 m) and put the ends of the epistyles into the middle of the wheels; also he fastened the ends by wooden cheeks; in the same way he put pivots into the bearings: so when the four digit material was drawn by oxen, the pivots placed in the bearings turned the wheels, and the epistyles shut in like axles in the wheels came, just like the shafts, to the site without delay. His model was the way in which rollers smooth the walks of the sports grounds. Nor could this have been done, unless in the first place there had been nearness—there is no more than eight thousand passus (11.8 km) from the quarry to the temple—nor any slope, but a flat ground only."

The "cheeks" were covers for the outside of the wheels to take the pivots; that was cheaper then cutting holes in all the epistyles. "The four digit material" shows that Metagenes used a frame similar to that used by his father.

> "10:2:13. Within our own memory, when the base of the enormous Apollo in the temple had become broken with age, they were afraid that the statue should fall and get broken, and made a contract for having a base cut from the same quarry. A man named Paconius undertook it. This base, however, was twelve feet long, 8 feet broad, six feet high (3.4 × 2.4 × 1.8 m). Paconius, trusting to his renown, did not transport it as Metagenes had done, but decided to make a contrivance on the same principle in another way. 14. He made wheels about 15 feet (4.4 m) and fastened the ends of the stone within them; then he fixed round sticks of two digits (3.7 cm) round the stone from wheel to wheel in a circle, so that the distance from stick to stick was not one foot (30 cm). Then he wound a rope round the sticks, and oxen were hitched and drew the rope. So when it was unwound, it turned the wheels, but it could not lead it straight along the right way, but it went away to one side. So it had to be brought back again. In this way Paconius used up the money in hauling out and back, so that he went bankrupt."

This attempt to do away with the frame was not successful, because the single rope could not give the great bobbin the right direction; it is possible that Paconius could have done it by two ropes and two teams of well trained oxen. It is unlikely, with twelve km to go, that he should have tied the rope to the cage; probably the rope took three or four turns round the sticks, and some men kept it taut behind the engine.

The rest of the chapter is a digression about how the quarry for this very fine marble was discovered.

Fig. 58 is a diagram of the water-drum described by Vitruvius 10:4:1–2, cut across
and seen from the inside. See text p. 150 sq.

Chapter 3 gives theoretical explanations of the effects of wheels,
pulleys and levers; some of the problems treated in the Mechanical
Problems are discussed. Interesting is the information that for a pair of
draught animals of unequal power the double-tree was not fastened by
the middle, but in such a way as to adjust the difference.

The next chapters, 4–7, deal with the transport of water.

> "10:4. Now I shall explain about the implements that are invented for the
> lifting of water, how they are made in various sorts. And first I shall speak of
> the drum. This does not lift the water high, but it pumps out quickly a great
> amount. An axle made on the lathe or by compasses, with its ends iron-plated,
> having round it for the rest of its length a drum made of boards joined together,
> is placed on posts that have iron plates in them under the heads of the axle. In
> the hollow of its drum are placed eight dividing walls that touch the axle and
> the farthest round of the drum, separating equal compartments of the drum.
> 2. Round its end are fastened lids leaving openings of half a foot (ca. 15 cm)
> for the water to come in. Also along the axle pigeon-holes are bored into each
> compartment at one end. It is tarred like a ship; it is turned by treading men;
> and taking in through the openings that are in the ends of the drum, it gives
> out through the pigeon-holes along the axle, where a wooden trough is placed
> with a gutter joined to it. In this way it provides a great amount of water for
> irrigating gardens or for managing saltpans."

Though no exact measures are given, except that of half a foot for
the water inlets, it is easy to reconstruct the general shape of this rotating
pump; fig. 58 is a diagram showing the lay-out of the drum. The "treading
men" simply stood on the drum and turned it with their naked feet.

F. M. Feldhaus (36) gives two figures illustrating this water-drum. One is a wall painting from Pompeji; it shows a slave turning a drum with his feet; but since the whole end of the drum is visible, it must be taken to be a water-snail (87). It is discussed on p. 154. The other figure is a diagram, but it is not in accordance with the text of Vitruvius: there are only four compartments; the inlets are through the sides, not in the ends; and the "pigeon-holes" lead into the hollow axle, from which the water comes out. It seems to have been reconstructed from the painting.

"10:4:3. But if it has to be lifted higher, the same method is adapted (?) like this: Let there be a wheel round an axle, of such a size that it fits the height for which there is need. Round the outer side of the wheel are fastened square boxes made tight with tar and wax. So when the wheel is turned by treading men, the full boxes, carried up on top, and returning to the bottom, all by themselves pour out into a container what they have carried up of water."

The buckets are placed on the side of the wheel, leaving the broad rim for the men to stand on, as is shown by the next verse.

"10:4:4. But if it is to be delivered in higher places still, round the axle of the wheel there is placed a double iron chain let down to the lowest level, with hanging bronze buckets on it, each holding a *congius* (3.3 l). So the turning of the wheel, by winding the chain round the axle, lifts the buckets up on top, which, when they are borne up over the axle, are forced to turn over and pour out into a container as much water as they have lifted out."

Since the bucket chain is placed round the axle, and the wheel is retained, it must mean that it is used for turning the axle. There is no description of any arrangement to prevent the chain from slipping on the axle.

The question of the endless chain is discussed on p. 199 sq.

"10:5. Wheels are also made in the rivers on the same principles as those mentioned above. Round their rims are placed paddles which, when they are pushed by the power of the river, go forward and force the wheel to turn and so, lifting by boxes and carrying up on high, being turned by the power of the river itself, without the treading of workers, they perform what is needed for use."

This sort of paddle wheel for lifting water from a flowing river is still in use. The word for "paddle", *pinna*, means feather, wing, fin; in short anything flat and thin.

"10:5:2. In the same way the watermills are turned, in which everything is the same, except that a toothed wheel is placed on one end of the axle. This, which stands upright on edge, is turned together with the wheel. Following that, a greater wheel, also toothed, is placed flat, on which is placed * * * * so the teeth of the wheel that is fastened to the axle by impinging on the teeth of the horizontal wheel brings about the turning of the mill-stones. In this implement a hanging funnel feeds grain to the mill-stones and the flour is ground by the same turning."

The editor reads *secundum id tympanum majus* ⟨*minus*⟩ *item dentatum planum est conlocatum:* "Following this greater wheel ⟨a smaller one,⟩ also toothed, is placed flat ..." It would be just as possible to read ... ⟨*minus*⟩ *majus* ...; the question of the gear is quite conjectural. One editor fills out the lacuna like this: "on which is placed ⟨an axle which has on its top a dove-tail, on which is placed a mill⟩", which gives just the sense needed.

For the dove-tail see p. 148-149.

Since Vitruvius does not mention any sort of building operations in connexion with the water-wheels, we must conclude that he is speaking of wheels driven by the current only, without dams, mill-ponds and other accessories.

Later on smaller brooks and rivers were used; but when the Goths, besieging Rome, cut off the water supply for the mills on the Janiculum, the situation was saved by the construction of "ship-mills", water-wheels mounted on ships anchored in the Tiber (84).

For the whole question of water-mills see L. A. Moritz: Grain-Mills and Flour in Classical Antiquity. Oxford 1958, ch. 15–16. I do not always agree with the author about technical details; but as a full and fair and well documented study of the subject it can hardly be recommended too strongly.

The gears are discussed on p. 202.

"10:6. There is also the method of the screw, which lifts a great amount of water, but does not lift it as high as a wheel. Its construction is made like this: A beam is taken, whose length in feet is made the same at its thickness in digits (16:1). It is made round by compasses. On the ends their circumferences are divided by compasses by fours and eights into eight parts, and these lines are so placed that when the beam is placed horizontally, the lines on each end correspond to each other in true level; and they are divided along the length in parts equal to one eighth of the circumference of the plank. Also on the horizontal plank lines are drawn from one end to the other in true level. In this way the distances both around and along become equal. So where the lines are drawn, which go along it, they make intersections, and the intersections make well-defined points. 2. When all this has been marked accurately, there is taken a thin strip of willow or cut out of chaste tree, which is smeared with liquid pitch and fastened on the first point of intersection. Then it is drawn diagonally towards

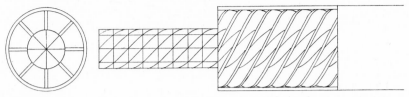

Fig. 59, a diagram of the Archimedean water-snail as described by Vitruvius 10:6. On the left it is seen from one end; the core has been divided by four diameters. The ends of the eight spirals show between the core and the outer boards; the resemblance to the water-drum is striking. Next is shown the core, divided into squares, and with the spirals drawn for the partitions; then the partitions themselves, before they are shut in by the outer boards. See text p. 152 sqq.

the next intersection of a line and a circle, and so going on regularly, passing over every point and wound round, it is fixed on each intersection, and thus comes back and is fastened, going from the first point to the eighth, to the same line in which its end was made fast. In this way, as far as it comes diagonally and through eight points, so far will it also come along the length to the eighth point. In the same way strips fastened diagonally through every space in length and roundness, going round through eight divisions in thickness, make canals and a true and natural imitation of a snail. 3. So along the same track other strips are fastened on the others, smeared with fluid pitch, and they are built up until the whole thickness is one eighth of the length. Round all over them boards are placed and joined together, so that they cover this winding. Then these boards are filled with pitch and bound with iron strips, so that they are not losened by the power of the water. The heads of the plank are of iron. To the right and left of the screw posts are set up which on either side on their ends carry fixed crossbeams. In these iron holes are made, and the pivots are put into them, and thus the screws are turned by treading men. 4. But it has to be set up at such a slope, that it corresponds to the way in which a Pythagorean triangle is drawn, that is, if the length is divided into 5 parts, the head of the screw should be lifted three of those; in this way there will be from the vertical to the bottom inlets a distance of 4 of these parts. But how this is to be done, the figure of it is drawn at the end of the book on the back side."

It is a pity that this figure does not exist any more; but the instructions on how to build the snail are so complete, that they would serve any craftsman to-day. See fig. 59.

The invention of this water-snail is ascribed to Archimedes by the ancient authors; in later times there has been a tendency to doubt this. I have collected the evidence (26) and shown that this doubt has no foundation at all. But in my enthusiasm about this implement I made one statement that is not quite correct. I wrote: "The water-snail is still in use, and its form has not changed since the time of Vitruvius, who describes it." But the water-snails found in Spanish mines (67) show a single spiral of copper in stead of the eight wooden windings described by Vitruvius. It is evident that the single copper plate would take up less room than the eight wooden spirals, and the question arises: why does Vitruvius use eight partitions, where one is enough? The answer is plain: because that was the original, Archimedean water-snail, and the copper spiral was introduced later, probably by the engineers in the copper mines. But why did Archimedes use eight canals? And once more the answer comes pat: because the water-snail was a modification of the water-drum described in 10:4:1–2 with its eight compartments. Archimedes, we are told, invented the snail during a stay in Egypt. Here, I take it, he saw the drum in use everywhere, and his studies of the screw lines and spirals gave him the idea of using the screw for transporting the water. And then, as so often happens, he just modified an already existing implement and did not at once arrive at the finished form with only one screw. The invention was a stroke of genius, and it comes almost as a relief to find that after all it was not made out of whole cloth, so to speak. I have always found that this was rather too much!

Vitruvius mentions all these pumps 5:12:5, where water has to be pumped out for the construction of a quai: "the place is emptied and dried by snails, wheels, and drums set up ...".

That the snail was turned by "treading men" using their bare feet on the snail itself is shown by a wall painting in Pompeji (36, 87) and a terracotta from Egypt (102). The wall painting, mentioned already p. 151, is not quite clear, and Feldhaus takes it to represent a drum. It is true that the cylinder on which the small slave is dancing seems to be more horizontal than sloping, but this may be due to the difficulties of the perspective. One end is hidden behind a pillar; but the other end, from which the water comes, is quite clear of the water, which is impossible, if a water-drum is meant. Also the stream of water comes from below the centre, which indicates that a snail is meant.

On the terracotta relief the drum has cleats for the man to tread on.

"10:6:4 (cont.): The water lifting implements made of wood, how they are constructed and how they get their movements to yield endless uses by turning, are described as clearly as I could do it, on this backside, so that they may be better known."

Here once more a figure is missing.

"10:7: What follows is to show Ctesibios's engine, which brings water up high. It is made of bronze. At its roots there are twin cylinders, not far apart, with pipes that hang together in the shape of a fork, coming together in the middle of a pot. In this pot there are made coins placed in the upper nostrils of the pipes with a clever joint, which by closing the opening of the nostrils do not let that go back which is forced into the pot by the wind. 2. Above the pot there is arranged a hood like an inverted funnel, and it is held on to the pot by a fastening with a wedge through it, so that the power of the blowing-in of water shall not force it to lift. Over this a pipe which is called riser pipe is fastened, going straight upwards. But the cylinders have below the lower nostrils of the pipes coins put in over their openings, which are in the bottom. 3. So from above in the cylinders male plungers, made smooth on the lathe and smeared and made tight with oil, when they, by rods and levers, move what there is there of air with the water, as the coins close the openings, force and compel by blowing with the pressures through the nostrils of the pipes the water into the pot, from which the hood receiving it by the wind presses it through the pipe upwards, and thus from a container placed in a lower place water it sent up for spouting."

Vitruvius has two difficulties to contend with: the lack of a suitable terminology for this kind of engine, and a false theory that air had something to do with the force pump, even when it was pumping water.

If we simply disregard all mention of air or wind, we shall get a very clear idea of the pump. There are two cylinders with plungers operated by horizontal levers and vertical connecting rods; since the cylinders are very near one another, it is unlikely that there is only one lever for both. The intakes are provided with valves like coins; the word *as* means a large coin, like a penny.

Heron, who wrote some 75 years later, uses two sorts of valves (57): square, vertical flap-valves, which he calls ἀσσάριον, *assarion*, clearly derived from the word *as*, and round, flat, horizontal lids to close the mouth of a vertical inlet, and kept in place by three pins. These lids are called τυμπάνια, disks, or πλατυσμάτια, small plates. It would seem then that the flap-valve is the older form, and was originally round, as in one of the British Museum pumps; so it was called *as* or *assarion*, and kept the name when it was made square. The *tympania* in Heron seem to be a later invention to fit the valve into the thickness of the bottom of the cylinder, as it is seen clearly from the MS figure, see fig. 60.

The outlet pipes from the cylinders come together like the tines of a pitchfork and enter the pot, which is a valve-chamber. The word *catinus* is translated by "air-chamber", but since the riser pipe goes out from its top, there can be no air in it. On the top of this valve-chamber

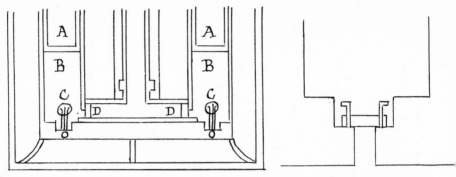

Fig. 60 illustrates Vitruvius 10:7; it is taken from Heron's Pneumatics, MS H, fol. 14r, where it shows the construction of the valves in the fire-pump, 1:28. I show only the lower part, and I have put in Roman letters for ease of reference. We see the plungers, AA, the cylinders, BB, the "coin-valves", CC, and the flap-valves, DD. The pump is standing at a bucket full of water. The two circles under the "coin-valves" indicate round inlets, narrower than the recess in which the "coins" are sitting. On the right I have shown, enlarged, a cut through one of these valves. See text p. 155 sqq.

is the "hood" like an inverted funnel; it is removable, so that it is possible to get at the valves. The word for "fastening", *fibula*, means any sort of tenon or lock; it is probably just a bronze pin with a slot for the wedge. Since there is only one, the other side of the hood must have been held either by a hinge or by a hook.

The whole thing is a regular force-pump, as they are used to-day; and if the inlets into the cylinders are placed in water, no air will be found in it once it begins to pump.

The cylinder and plunger were invented by Ktesibios (131), who used them first of all for pumping air for his water-organ and other pneumatic devices. When he constructed the force-pump for water, he probably thought that all pumping had to be done with the help, in some way, of air, and this is why Vitruvius, who used Ktesibios's own book on Pneumatics, brings in air, *aër*, or wind, *spiritus*, where they really have nothing to do at all.

The cylinders have to stand in water; there are no pipes leading from the bottom of the cylinder to a stream or pond; Vitruvius says expressly that the water is pumped up from a container. This is in accordance with the description of the force-pump in Philon's Pneumatics (98) and the fire-pump in Heron's Pneumatics (58). The suction-pump was not yet invented at this time.

Three bronze pumps at least have survived from Antiquity. Two of them are found in the British Museum (9). In one of them there are flap-valves, the other has spindle-valves, a decided improvement. The third pump, found in Chiaruggia in 1795, was published the same year. The text and the figure are reprinted in Heron's Pneumatics, p. XXXIII and XXXV. It was provided with flap-valves and seems to have stood in the water.

A question asked of the British Museum brought me an answer by Mr. D.E. Strong, assistant keeper, to the effect that neither of the pumps preserved in the Museum showed any signs of having been connected with pipes from their inlets; they must have stood in water also.

The next chapter deals with the water-organ, which lies outside the scope of this book; but we take up the thread with ch. 9.

"10:9. The plan of writing now comes to a method, not useless, but transmitted with great earnestness by our ancestors, by which, sitting in a carriage on the road or sailing on the sea, we can know how many miles we have travelled. This will be in this way. The wheels that are on the carriage should have a diameter through the middle of four feet [and one sixth], so that, when the wheel has a fixed mark on it and begins going forward from it to make a turning on the surface of the road, when it reaches that mark from which it began to turn, it shall have gone through a length of 12 and a half feet exactly. 2. When this has been arranged like this, a drum is firmly fixed on the hub of the wheel on the inside, having a single tooth projecting from the rim of its roundness. But above, on the body of the carriage, a box is fastened firmly, with a drum turning, placed upright, and sitting on an axle, in the rim of which drum there are made four hundred teeth equally spaced and engaging the tooth in the lower drum. Further, on the side of the upper drum there is placed another tooth projecting beyond the teeth. 3. But above it another, horizontal ⟨drum⟩, toothed in the same way, is placed, held by another box, with teeth engaging the tooth that was fastened to the side of the second drum, and in this drum there are holes, as many as the number of miles the carriage can go in one day's journey. More or less does not matter. And in all these holes round pebbles are placed, and in the case of this wheel, or if it is a box, should be made a single hole which has a pipe, through which the pebbles that were placed in this drum, when they have come to this place, can fall one by one into the body of the carriage and into a bronze bowl placed under it. 4. So when the wheel going forward takes with it the lower drum, and its tooth at every turn by striking on them makes the teeth of the upper drum go along, it will bring about ⟨that⟩ when the lower one has been turned 400 times, the upper drum is turned once, and the tooth that is fixed to its side will move one tooth of the horizontal drum forward. So when by 400 turns of the lower drum the upper one makes one turn, the journey will have been a length of five thousand feet, which is one thousand *passus*. It follows that as many pebbles as fall will tell by the sound that one mile has been accomplished. Also the number of pebbles collected from below will indicate the total of the number of miles in the day's journey. 5. For sailings the same is accomplished likewise in the same way with a few alterations. For out through the sides an axle is put forth with its heads projecting outside the ship, in which are placed wheels with a diameter of four feet, having outstanding paddles fastened to their rims touching the water. Also the middle of the axle in the middle of the ship has a drum with one tooth projecting beyond its roundness. In this place is set up a box carrying a drum with 400 equally spaced teeth engaging the tooth of the drum that is fixed to the axle, also having fixed to its side one tooth projecting beyond its roundness. 6. Above, contained in another box fastened to it, (is) a horizontal drum, toothed in the same way, with which teeth the tooth that is fastened to the side of the drum that is placed upright ⟨engages⟩, so that the tooth striking on those teeth that are in the horizontal drum, one by each turn, turns round the horizontal drum. But in the horizontal drum holes should be made, in which round pebbles are placed. In the case of this wheel, or if it is a box, a single hole is bored with a pipe through which the pebble set free from the obstacles will indicate by the sound when it has fallen into a bronze bowl. 7. So when the ship is driven forward by oars or the blowing wind, the paddles that are on the wheels, touching the water running past, forced by the strong backwards drive, will turn the wheels; these, however, in turning will move the axle, the axle the drum, whose tooth going round for each turn by striking one by one the teeth of the second drum will cause slower turnings. So when the wheels have been turned 400 times by the paddles, the drum taken round once will drive by the tooth that is fastened to its side a tooth on the horizontal drum. It follows that the turning of the horizontal drum whenever it takes the pebbles to the hole will send them through the pipe. So it will show both by sound and by number the length of the sailing in miles."

We may find Vitruvius long-winded and over-careful; but no one shall say that he does not describe his hodometer so that we can understand it.

Mathematically the thing is in order: a diameter of 4 will give a circumference of 12.5 as near as necessary, 4π being 12.5664. 400 by 12.5 make 5000; 5 Roman feet are one *passus*, a double step; and 1000 *passus* are one Roman mile. But how about practice?

Vitruvius is not describing a thing he has seen; he has taken it from a book. Whether we imagine the teeth as triangular or as cylindrical pegs, we cannot reckon less than 2 cm for each tooth, or peg + interval; the circumference of the drum then becomes 8 m, and the diameter 2.55 m, which does not look very probable. In fig. 61 I have sketched how the wheel would look on a Roman carriage with four wheels of 4 feet. The proportions are taken from a relief (69).

This enormous wheel is quite unnecessary, since two wheels of 20

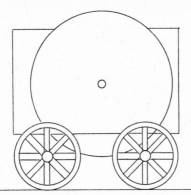

Fig. 61 illustrates Vitruvius 10:11. It shows a carriage (from an ancient relief) with the enormous wheel necessary for the hodometer drawn to scale. It does not look very probable. See text p. 157 sqq.

teeth each would have the same effect, each with a diameter of 12.7 cm. Also there must have been some sort of pawl to hold the wheel in a jolting, springless carriage. I think that we must regard it as an arm-chair invention.

Dr. Derek de Solla Price has criticized the hodometer (101); he writes p. 84: "Thus Vitruvius writes of a wheel 4 feet in diameter and having 400 teeth being turned by a 1-toothed pinion on a cart axle, but it is very doubtful whether such small teeth, necessarily separated by about $^3/_8$ inch, would have the requisite ruggedness." The dimension of 4 feet is given only for the wheel of the cart, while no dimension is given for the drum with the 400 teeth. But if we make a proper dimension of the teeth our starting point, the size of the drum becomes impossible, as I have shown; so this remark by dr. Price really supports my view.

As for the application to a ship, it would have no chance of being right except in a flat calm and on a sea without currents. The problem of getting the axle out through the side of the ship without water coming in if the ship heeled over or the waves splashed against it is not even mentioned. I refuse to believe in it.

Heron's hodometer

In Heron's Dioptra (51), written about one hundred years later, we have a hodometer that looks more likely.

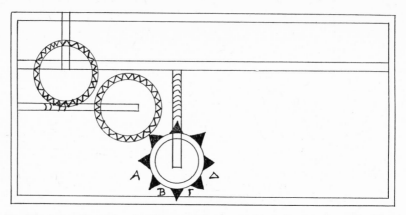

Fig. 62a is the illustration for Heron's Dioptra ch. 34; it is taken from the Mynas codex in Paris. It shows the toothed wheel to be turned one tooth at a time by a pin (not shown), and carrying a screw engaging another wheel carrying a screw, which engages a third wheel, whose axle should carry a pointer. See text p. 159 sqq.

"34. We think that it will be fitting for the dioptrical treatise also to measure the distances on the ground by the so-called road-measurer, so that you do not measure by using a chain or a band laboriously and slowly, but riding in a vehicle learn the distances mentioned from the turning of the wheels. Those before us explained some methods by which this could be done; so it is possible to form a judgment about the implement described by us and those described by our predecessors." (See fig. 62a). "Let there be a frame-work like a small chest, in which all the fittings that we are going to describe will be housed; in the bottom of the box .... is ΑΒΓΔ, made of brass, having fixed on it the pins mentioned; for those there should be a hole in the bottom of the box, through which a pin, fixed on the hub of one of the wheels of the vehicle, for every turn coming through the hole in the bottom of the box pushes forward one of the pins, so that the next pin takes up again the same position as the preceding pin, and so on for ever. So it will happen that when the wheel has made eight turns, the disk with the pins has made one revolution. Let there then be a screw connected with the said disk with the pins, fixed to its centre at right angles, having its other end in a cross-bar fastened in the sides of the box. Against the said screw there should be found a toothed disk, whose teeth fit the spiral of the screw, and of course set up a right angles to the bottom, and having also fixed on it an axle, whose ends turn in the sides of the box. One part of the axle should again have cut into it a spiral so that it is a screw. And once more against this screw there should be placed a toothed disk, obviously placed parallel to the bottom of the box, with an axle fitted to it, one ⟨end⟩ of which should turn in the bottom of the box, the other in a joist fastened to the sides of the box; this axle also should have at its other end a screw which again is engaged with the teeth of another disk, which obviously is placed at right angles to the bottom. And so it goes on as

far as we want, or as far as there is room for it in the box; for the more disks
and screws there are, the longer will be found the road that is measured. For
every screw will by a single turn move one tooth of the disk engaged by it; so
that when the screw connected with the disk with the pins has made one turn,
which means eight times the circumference of the wheel, it has moved one tooth
of the disk engaged with it. For instance, if the disk engaged has thirty teeth,
when it is turned once by the screw, it will denote 240 turns of the wheel. And
again, for every turn of the said toothed disk, the screw fixed to it will turn once,
and one tooth of the disk engaged by the screw will be moved. If then also this
disk has 30 teeth, though it is clear that it could also have more, when it is turned
once, it will indicate 7200 turns of the wheel; if then the wheel has a circumference
of 10 ells, it will be 72.000 ells, that is 180 stades. And this is found on the second
disk; when there are more of them, and the number of teeth is augmented, many
times the length of road will be found to be measured. But it should be put
together in such a way that the instrument cannot indicate a much larger way
than that which can be travelled by the vehicle in a single day, for then it is possible each day after measuring the way travelled that day to start from the beginning again on the next day."

The Dioptra is a treatise on surveying; it begins with a description
of an instrument, a combined theodolite and water-level, and goes on
to give instructions on its use for a great many practical purposes.
Then, at the end of the book, Heron adds an appendix on other methods
of measuring land.

That the hodometers, "road-measurers", described by "those before
him" include that of Vitruvius, is very likely; Heron does not say that
they made instruments, merely that they set forth methods, which seems
to indicate that they were merely speculation. Nor does Heron state
that his instrument has ever been in use; he invites comparison between
his description and those of his predecessors.

He begins with a house for the working parts; it should look like "a
small chest" κιβώτιον; so he calls it κιβωτάριον, which means the
same, but is another word. I have used the word "box". Next comes
a lacuna, which is very easy to fill out: a disk of brass with eight projecting pins is placed about an axle turning in the bottom of the box;
the disk itself should be very near the bottom. In figure 62a, which is
taken from the Mynas Codex in Paris, the pins, σκυτάλια, are shown
as triangular projections from the rim of the disk; and they would
serve the purpose. The Greek word is a diminutive of σκυτάλη, often
used for "handspake", and denotes pins sitting at intervals along the
rim of the wheel. The teeth of the toothed disks in the hodometer elsewhere are always ὀδόντες, "teeth", meaning probably triangular teeth

touching at their bases, as indicated in the drawing. The driving pin on the hub of the wheel is called περόνη, "round peg", perhaps because, it is sitting alone by itself. The wheel of the vehicle is τροχός, "wheel" while the toothed wheels of the instrument are τύμπανοι, "drums" or "disks". The disk with the pins carries a screw on its axle, which turns in the bottom of the box and in a horizontal bar, as is shown clearly in the figure. This is because the lid of the box has to be opened when we read the position of the disks.

The disk turned by this screw has a horizontal axle, since itself is vertical, and this can turn in the sides of the box, because they are fixed. The next disk, however, being horizontal, has to have its axle in the bottom of the box and in a horizontal "joist"; this is not clearly shown in the figure. Two different words are used for these horizontal elements for carrying the bearings; in either case it must be a narrow board, for a full partition would interfere with the reading of the disks.

The mathematical computation is correct. The circumference of the wheel is 10 ells. One ell is 46.2 cm, so the diameter of the wheel is 130 cm, quite a probable size. Only Heron does not mention it at all: the circumference is the thing! The first disk makes one turn for eight turns of the wheel, the second disk with 30 teeth indicates 240 turns; a third disk with 30 teeth indicates 7200 turns or 72000 elles; one stade is 400 ells, so 72.000 ells are 180 stades or 33.3 km, since one stade is 185 m.

This is the theory, which is always nice and green; but Heron has something to say about the practice, which may take on another colour.

> "But since the turn of every screw does not turn the engaging teeth exactly or precisely, we turn for a test the first screw, until the toothed disk engaged with it has made one turn, counting meanwhile how many times the screw is turned. Let this for instance be 20 turns, by which the disk engaging it has made one turn; but that had 30 teeth; so the 20 turns of the disk with the pins have moved 30 teeth of the disk engaging the screw; the 20 turns move 160 pins, and so many turns of the wheel; that will be 1600 ells. If 30 teeth measure 1600 ells, then one tooth of the said disk marks 53^1/$_3$ ells of the road. So when the toothed disk begins to move and is found to have moved 15 teeth, it indicates a stretch of 800 ells, that is two stades. So we shall write in the middle of the said toothed disk "53^1/$_3$ ells"; and we compute the same thing also for the other toothed disks and write the figures; so that for each of them, when they have moved a number of teeth, we know the stretch indicated."

The endless screws described by Heron in his Mechanics 2:6, 16, 18, 29, were made of wood and in such dimensions that it would be possible to obtain a good fit between the screw and the wheel; here the theory holds good: one turn of the wheel equals as many turns of the screw as there are teeth on the wheel. But for the comparatively small screws and cog-wheels of the hodometer a real fit could not be obtained with the tools available at the time; there were no screw-cutting dies for making the screws, and no dividing heads for making the cogs; everything was made piece-meal and by hand. No wonder if they did not always fit.

Dr. Derek Price cannot accept this construction at all; he writes (101): "Again, Hero mentions a wheel of 30 teeth which, because of imperfections, might need only 20 turns of a single helix worm to turn it! Such statements behove caution and one must consider whether we have been misled by the 16th- and 17th-century editions of these authors, containing reconstructions now often cited as authoritative but then serving as working diagrams for practical use in that age when the clock was already a familiar and complex mechanism."

Our text for Heron's Dioptra is found in the Mynas Codex in Paris (50); it is written in the 11. or 12. century A.D., so "the 16th- and 17th-century editions" with their reconstructions have no chance of misleading us about what Heron wrote. There is not the slightest reason for rejecting this description as spurious, unless we consider it as mechanically impossible. (If we do, we would also have to consider how a 16th- or 17th-century editor came to write it at all.) That Heron used worm-and-wheel gear made of brass is shown by his description of the dioptra; there are two gears: one to turn and lock the vertical column carrying the theodolite, another to turn and hold the half-circle carrying the sighting-rod. So Heron must have had some experience of the vagaries of the worms and wheels in brass of his time. And what should have led him to write this piece unless it was an actual experience? We shall have to let it stand.

In fig. 62b I have tried to draw a hodometer with five axles. In A it is seen from above, in B from one of the long sides, in C from one end. The axles 1 and 5 can be carried by the same board, the axle 3 has a board of its own, lifted to make room for the cog-wheel on axle 4. The lid can be lifted, when the instrument has to be read. But this is an unnecessary trouble, as we see from the following text.

"So that we shall not, when we want to read the length of the road, have to open the box to look at the teeth of each disk, we shall show how we can find the length of the road through the surface of any box by pointers going round.

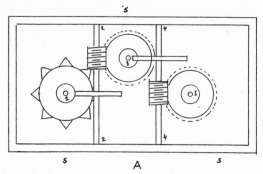

Fig. 62b is a diagram of a hodometer with 5 axles, as described by Heron, Dioptra ch. 34. A is the aspect from above, B from the side, C from one end. The lid is marked 1. See text p. 163 sqq.

The said toothed disks are so placed that they do not touch the sides of the box, but their axles stick out beyond the walls; these projections should be square, so that they can carry pointers by means of square holes; in this way when the disk is turned with the axle, the pointer will also be turned; so its point going round traces a circle on the other side of the same board, which circle we will divide into as many parts as there are teeth on the disk inside. The pointer should be of such a size that it traces a larger circle, so that the interval between the teeth are drawn larger; also the drawn circle shall have the same inscription as the disk inside; and in this way we can from the outer surface learn about the length of the road travelled. If it is not possible that all the disks do not touch the sides of the box, because they get in the way of each other, or because of the screws engaging them, or for some other reason, we place each of them so far apart, that they do not get in the way.

Now since some of the toothed disks are parallel to the bottom, others at right angles, so also some of the circles traced by the pointers will be on the upright sides of the box, others on the lid. For this reason then one of the upright sides that does not have the circles must be a lid, so that that which seems a lid should be a side."

Turning once more to fig. 62b we see that the axles 1, 3, 5 can come up through the lid (1 in B and C), while 2 and 4 can come out through one of the sides (s, s in A and C); either of the short sides will do for a lid, since they carry no axles.

It is clear that if the disks come out through the sides of the box, we cannot make the dial larger than the corresponding disk, so we have to space the axles and disks anew for the new arrangement.

It is less clear why Heron does not give us the correct solution at once. Without this addition about the pointers, I should not hesitate to accept the hodometer as an actual instrument, in view of the proposed

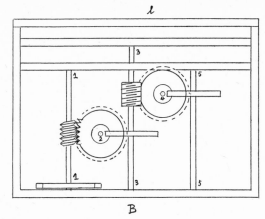

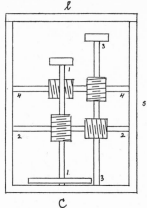

B   C

test of the screws; but with this addition it looks more like a theoretical invention, and the experience of the screw must have been made elsewhere. Another possibility is that the first form was in actual use, but when Heron wrote it down, he discovered how it might be improved, and added the pointers. That would be entirely like him.

The next chapter of the Dioptra, ch. 35, shows how to find the distance between Alexandria and Rome by observing the same eclipse of the moon from both cities; there is no ch. 36; after ch. 35 comes, as ch. 37, the description of the Barulkos, already discussed here on p. 24 sqq; it has nothing to do in this place. But it is followed by a ch. 38, which describes a hodometer for a ship. It begins without any sort of introduction. See fig. 63a.

"38. Let there be, turning in some bearings, a screw AB, to which is fastened [sic] a toothed disk Δ with ⟨81⟩ teeth. Let there be fastened to this ⟨the disk E⟩ with ⟨9⟩ teeth. Parallel with that there should be Z with 100 teeth; fixed to that there should be H with 18 teeth. Engaged with that there should be Θ with 72 teeth. To this also should be fastened K with 18 teeth. In the same way Λ with 100 teeth; [by which also another with 30 teeth], on which should sit a pointer to show the number of stades [sic]. Let there be made a winged wheel, M, with a circumference of ... *passus*, turned in the lathe, taking the same time as the ship. ... (unintelligible) ...; being capable of letting one tooth of Δ pass for every turn of M. Now it is clear that when the ship has sailed 100 miles, the disk Λ will have made one turn; so if a circle round the centre of Λ is divided into 100 parts, the pointer fastened to Λ, going round the said circle, will show the single movements of the ship."

This chapter is not very easy to get right, because the tradition is rather faulty. The general lay-out of this "patent log" is quite simple:

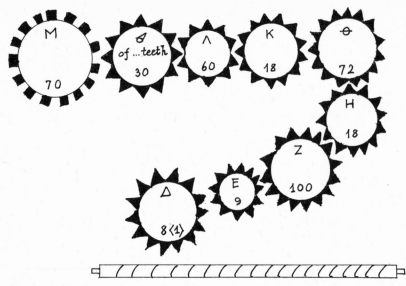

Fig. 63a is the illustration for Heron's Dioptra, ch. 38; it is taken from the Mynas codex in Paris and shows the hodometer for a ship. It is discussed in the text p. 165 sqq., where it is argued that it cannot have been drawn by Heron himself.

there is a paddle-wheel outside the ship, turning a screw inside; this screw turns a cog-wheel, and the reduction gear consists of cog-wheels, like the barulkos, and ends in a pointer making one turn for every 100 miles. These are Roman miles, of 1.479 km, and so the circumference of the paddle-wheel is given in *passus;* unfortunately the number is missing.

According to the text, the reduction gear consists of a screw, engaging a wheel with 81 teeth, and of the following pairs: Δ 81 + E 9; Z 100 + H 18; Θ 72 + K 18; then Λ 100 with a pointer. An anonymous wheel with 30 teeth fixed to Λ is an obvious error, which may be explained by the fact that the letter Λ stands for the number 30 in Greek.

The figure, redrawn here as fig. 63a, shows the screw, all by itself, and eight cog-wheels, placed one after the other, not, as in the barulkos, two and two on their axles. Last comes the paddle-wheel, quite unconnected with the screw. Each cog-wheel carries its letter and another letter indicating the number of teeth; where the text is at fault, it has been supplied from the figure. We find: Δ 80; E 9; Z 100; H 18; Θ 72, K 18; Λ 60; ♂ 30; M 70. On ♂ is written οδοντων, "of (so and so many) teeth".

The wheel Δ carries the number 80, represented by the letter Π; the editor has supplied, quite correctly, I think, for the text another figure, to make it 81; it would be Π A. On Λ, the letter Ξ, meaning 60, cannot be a slip of the pen for P, which means 100. The last, quite superfluous cog-wheel, with 30 teeth, corresponds to the text; the number 70 on the paddle-wheel M is quite absurd.

If we compute the ratio from the figures of the text, we find 1:45.000; if we take the figures of the drawing, correcting 80 into 81, we find 1:27.000, neither of which seems likely, since we should expect a whole number of *passus* for the circumference of the paddle-wheel. A circumference of 4.5 *passus* would give a diameter of 1.45 *passus* or 2.5 m; 2.7 *passus* correspond to 0.85 *passus* or 1.25 m.

There are two minor difficulties in the text. One is that the screw is called AB, the first wheel Δ; but the leaving out of a letter, Γ, is very unusual. The second is that the wheel is said to be fixed to the screw, συμφυές; this is absurd, it should be engaged with the screw, παρακεί-μενον. But we cannot add a wheel, Γ, engaged with the screw and fixed to Δ, for the great wheel of 81 teeth is the one to be driven by the screw, as we also find it stated later in the text.

And now we must try to find out what this thing is, anyway. It is clear that it does not belong with the Dioptra and the hodometer of ch. 34. The Dioptra ends with ch. 35 or the missing ch. 36; the Barulkos, ch. 37, has been added here, as it is in the Mechanics, though it does not belong; but it is, after all, a work by Heron himself. The construction of the ships' hodometer is built on that of the barulkos; but it has nothing to do with the mechanical problem of the Barulkos, that of lifting or dragging heavy burdens. Also there seems to be no reason why Heron, if he wanted to adapt his road hodometer for use on a ship, should change from the cog-and-screw drive to a cog-and-wheel drive. The road hodometer counts stades, the Greek measure of length; but the ships' hodometer is constructed for Roman miles, though the pointer is first said to indicate stades. From all this I conclude that this chapter is not written by Heron, but is an armchair invention, made from the Barulkos by somebody else. For proof we have only to compare the figure with those of Heron. We have three figures of instruments of this kind; two from the Barulkos (fig. 5 and 6), and one from the Mechanics 2:21 (figs. 29a, b). In spite of the great difference between the figure for the barulkos in the Mechanics (fig. 5) and that in the Dioptra (fig. 6), they belong together and give a far better picture than the

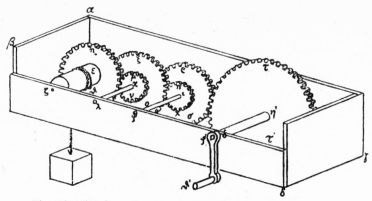

Fig. 63b. Nix's figure for Heron's Mechanics 1:1. Compare fig. 5.
See text p. 168.

figure of the hodometer (fig. 63a), where all the pinions and wheels are shown one after another, and the screw and the paddle-wheel are placed far apart. It seems unthinkable that this figure should have been drawn by the same man who drew the barulkos, fig. 6. It may be objected that the figure was made from the text, since it includes the last wheel of 30 teeth, which is an interpolation. But since the text refers to the figure by letters, there must have been a figure with it from the beginning, and it is conceivable that a scribe should have put in an extra wheel which he found in the text, but not that anyone should have changed a figure from something like fig. 6 to that of fig. 63a.

I have said before that an edition of an illustrated text is unsatisfactory, as long as the illustrations are not reproduced in their original shape. I wish now to drive the lesson home; so I reproduce the figures from the Teubner edition for comparison with the originals as I have reproduced them. See figs. 63b–f. The reader can see for himself how impossible it is to form any reliable conclusion on the basis of these interpretations alone.

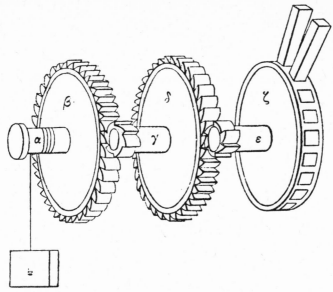

Fig. 63c. Nix's figure for Heron's Mechanics 2:21. Compare figs. 29a, b.
See text p. 168.

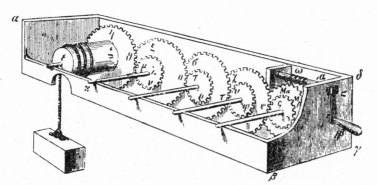

Fig. 63d. Hultsch's figure of Heron's barulkos, from Pappos p. 1060. Compare fig. 7.
See text p. 168.

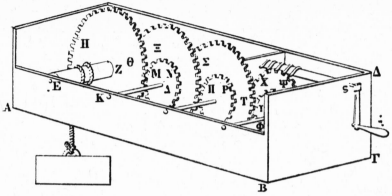

Fig. 63e. Schoene's figure of Heron's barulkos, from his Dioptra, ch. 37. Compare fig. 6. See text. p. 168.

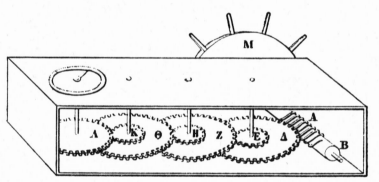

Fig. 63f. Schoene's figure of the ships' hodometer, from Heron's Dioptra, ch. 38. Compare fig. 63a. See text p. 168.

Vitruvius goes on to describe war-engines: siege-towers, battering rams, and catapults; but these I am going to discuss later on.

Oreibasios

As I have said already, on p. 12, Oreibasios lived about 362 A.D. and wrote a large compendium on medicine (88). What interests us here are the engines for resetting dislocated limbs, because they show in use contrivances mentioned by Heron, but not employed by the engineers. The inference from the text is that the surgeons were not very content with the engines they had, and caught eagerly at every new invention to improve them.

Some of these re-setting machines lived on as implements for torture since they could cause great pain without lasting or visible injury. In these times when analgesia was unknown the patients had to undergo great hardship to ensure an effective cure.

Oreibasios, copying Heliodoros, a surgeon of the 2. century A.D., first speaks in general of the re-setting engines, and then gives us a list of all the parts of which they are composed. He tells about the tortoises, the sliding parts of the engines, that they are made so as to make the stretchings even and without lesions on the bodies of the patients, and that they move slowly, like the animals themselves. He goes on:

"49:4:52. Since as a rule the tortoises are moved by screws, I shall next explain the construction and effect of the screws. 53. Screws, then, in engines have been devised for moving other mechanical parts, such as wheels and tortoises, so that their stretchings may be without lesions and even. 54. Of the screws some are square, others lentil-shaped; these shapes have their names from the screw-threads, not from the form of the stick, for every screw is round, turned to the shape of its outside; but the screws differ from each other by the screw-thread, from which some are called square, others lentil-shaped. 55. Square is the screw that has square screw-threads, both the furrow and the ridge; (such are the screws in the engine of Andreas;) 56. lentil-shaped are those that have the furrows narrow in the bottom, broad upwards, and the ridges broad at the bottom, but tapering towards the top, like a lentil cut in half. 57. For this screw is called lentil-shaped from this figure. 58. The square and lentil-shaped screws being like this, they are made to move different contrivances; for the square screws move tortoises, the lentil-shaped screws by preference wheels, but at times also tortoises by the so-called female screws.

49:5. How a square screw moves a tortoise

1. Let the construction be like this, as in the tortoises in the engine of Andreas: each is bored through, and the screw is passed through the hole, but inside the hole an iron or bronze plate has been driven into the tortoise. This plate is called "tooth". 2. Now this tooth of the tortoise is engaged with the screw-thread of

the screw; accordingly the result is that, caught up by the turning of the screw one way or another, the plate called the little tooth, reaching round the screw in the hollow screw-thread itself, will move the tortoise. 3. Of these square screws some are single, others double. 4. A single screw is one that is cut by one screw-thread and moves one tortoise; a double screw is such a one as is cut by two screw-threads and moves two tortoises. 5. Such is the screw in the great frame, the engine of Andreas, for the middle part of the stick, between the cross-pieces, is cut by antithetic screw-threads, so that, according to how the screw is turned, the tortoises will either go from the middle towards the cross-pieces, or come together from the cross-pieces towards the middle. 6. There is also a double screw in the so-called *caduceus*, cut from the upper end right down to the other end by antithetic screw-threads, which also moves two tortoises, as ⟨it will be explained⟩ in the description of the instrument. 7. The lentil-shaped screw moves a wheel; for the screw-threads of the screw engaging the teeth of the wheel turn the implement; which screw, turned by a peg or a handle, and engaging the teeth of the wheel, moves the implement. 8. Sometimes the same screw moves a tortoise, but not by a tooth, as does the square screw, but being held in the so-called female screw, which female screw is contrived in the tortoise itself; for the hole itself through the tortoise, that which receives the screw, is cut out by screw-threads corresponding to those of the lentil-shaped screw, so that the projecting threads of the lentil-shaped screw are caught in the hollow threads of the female screw, and the projecting threads of the female screw are admitted into the ⟨hollow threads of the lentil-shaped screw⟩. 9. The result is that by the turning of the screw, the screws being engaged by their screw-threads, the tortoise will be moved now up and now down."

In vers 8 "the same screw" means "a lentil-shaped screw", not the same screw as the one that turns the wheel.

Andreas, who lived at the same time as Archimedes, had to use a *tylos* for his screw; later engines would have the female screw, once the screw-cutter was invented.

The rest of the chapter contains a list of the fixed parts of these engines in general.

"49:6. From the works of Galenos. On engines

For resetting joints the so-called bank of Hippocrates alone is enough; but if somebody wants to use others, then for travelling the so-called compound pulley is apt (it is said to be an invention by Archimedes), but for use in town, if it is to be upright, the engine called that of Tekton or that of Andreas; if horizontal, the bank of Hippocrates.

49:7. About the mechanical chest

1. It seems to me quite a good invention of the more recent physicians, the instrument like a chest for treating fractures, whether a thigh-bone or a shin-bone has been broken; it has at one end an axle, towards which the ends of the loops stretching the limb are brought and wound round; the loops themselves are to

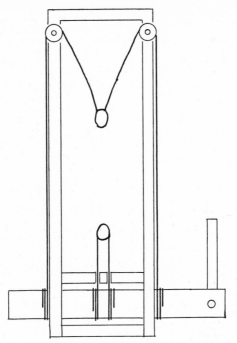

Fig. 64 is a diagram of the mechanical chest, Oreibasios 49:6. See text p. 172 sqq.

be placed round the ends of the bone of the patient. 2. They consist of two full-length ropes, so that there are four parts to each of the loops, two to the right, and two to the left. 3. Of these parts those from the lower loop you have to pass through some holes that are in the lower end of the chest and put them round the axle; those from the upper loop you have to pass first to the upper part of the chest and then take these also out through some holes that are in its sides; and the holes should have pulley-wheels in them. 4. Then from each side on the outside of the chest you have to lead down the said ends of the loops and bring them to the axle; for when this has been arranged in this way, one turn of the axle stretches those two loops equally: downwards the one that is laid round the lower end of the bone to be pulled down, the other upwards, so that after the stretching is done, you still are free to adjust the pulling-apart of the loops, either by tightening the pull or by loosening; for the loop on the lower parts of the limb the axle stretches by a direct pull, but the upper one by what is called movement and antimovement."

Fig. 64 shows my reconstruction of Galenos's Mechanical Chest. The description of the construction is quite clear; less clear is the reason for having double ropes everywhere.

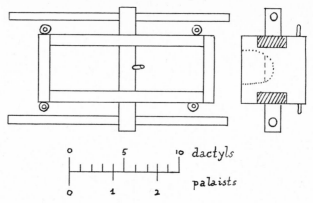

0   5   10   *dactyls*

0   1   2   *palaists*

Fig. 65a is a diagram of the spanner of Neileus, with the improvement by Herodotos, from Oreibasios 49:8:1–7. See text p. 174 sq.

The pull between the loops must be the same, whether one or two are pulled, and whether both are pulled by the same axle or not.

In all these engines it must be kept in mind, that for resetting a dislocated joint a pull was sufficient; but for treating a fracture, the pull had to be kept up while the bone was put into place and the fracture bandaged.

Galenos, from whom this description is taken, lived from 129 to 199 A.D.

"49:8. From Heliodoros. The bank of Neileus

The bank of Neileus is made up of the so-called square, oblong spanners; for it has two sides of four palaists (31 cm), in breadth one palaist (7.7 cm), in thickness one daktyl (1.9 cm), held together by their ends by the so-called cross-pieces; these cross-pieces have the same breadth and thickness as the sides, but are one palaist (7.7 cm) long. 2. It follows logically that when the sides are of four palaists, the cross-pieces of one palaist, the shape of the spanner will be an oblong quadrangle. 3. It is possible, if you like, to make the sides shorter than the measure given, that is, if the engine works with a single axle. 4. In round holes cut out opposite one another in the middle of the sides there is a projecting axle, with a peg in its middle, but with handles on the projecting round ends, made of bronze or iron, ten daktyls (19 cm) long. 5. The spanner also has four rings nailed to the sides, two above and two below."

Fig. 65a shows my reconstruction of the spanner of Neileus; the improvement by Herodotos is shown in dotted lines. It is meant to be lashed to a bank, if it is used in the clinic; otherwise to a ladder.

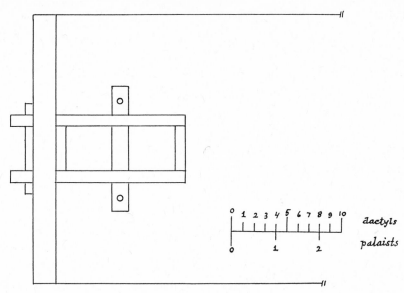

Fig. 65b is a diagram of the spanner of Neileus, mounted on a bank by Heliodoros, from Oreibasios 49:8:15. See text p. 175 sq.

"6. The old design, the one made by Neileus, son of Neileus, is like this; but one Herodotos, being a practical man, hollowed out the cross-pieces on the forward side in the middle, in the shape of a sigma (C), so that the cords going down from the bodies being pulled to the peg on the axle should not be worn by the outstanding edges, but should be pulled straight by it. 7. Such then was Herodotos; as we have received this tale, so we give it. It is said that the practical Pasikrates, living in Sidon, has designed this spanner, held by a statue, but using a different design; while the frame was the same, the spanner had on the projecting, round ends of the axle plaitings of bronze serpents, whose heads and tails were standing out opposite ways. 8. What was the purpose of these serpents? They were made in stead of the handles for turning the axle, while the engine in Sidon had the middle cross-piece pierced by round holes corresponding to the peg on the axle. 9. It is clear that those holes had the same function as the invention of Herodotos, that is, that the cords from the bodies to be pulled should come straight through the holes from the axles. 10. Pasikrates also stated further that there were four wheels of bronze round the axle, put on it near the sides, two inside, two outside; for the sides were also pierced according to the arrangement of the teeth. 11. They were of use for this: that bolts, after the sufficient stretching, put into the interstices between the teeth, should lock the axle for the use in setting limbs. 12. Those of a later time have discarded the wheels, they have bored through the opposite sides from the outside, and they have also bored round at some intervals into the rounded parts of the axle, so

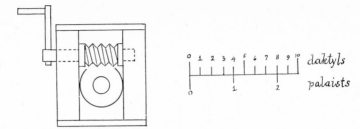

Fig. 66. The chest of Nymphodoros. This is my reconstruction illustrating Oreibasios 49:21:1–7. See text p. 176 sq.

that pins put in can keep the axle fixed for the purpose mentioned. 13. But I myself, because the pins will fall out, I have, for the use mentioned, fastened pawls to the sides and have made in the round ends of the axle holes all round at intervals corresponding to the holes in the sides, so that whenever I wanted to fix the axle for a resetting, I would lock the pawl in the corresponding hole. 14. The general construction of the frame is the same; but I have constructed also the frame in another way; while the dimensions of the sides are the same, I have moved the lower cross-piece upwards, letting the lower ends of the sides stick out one palaist (7.7 cm) beyond the cross-piece, and I have placed the axle in the middle of what is called the *lumen* of the cross-pieces. 15. And in one of the prescribed steps at one end of the board I have cut out oblong, rectangular holes, so that the ends of the sides described are fitted into these holes; and in the sides themselves I have bored holes opposite each other right through, so that a peg fixed in the holes can keep the bank together. This is the construction of the engine; now we come to the movement."

Fig. 65b shows my reconstruction of the spanner of Neileus as improved by Heliodoros; it illustrates Oreibasios 49:8:14–15. The bank itself I have made 2 ells broad (92 cm); this is the dimension of the bank of Hippokrates (see p. 184). It is clear that either the axle must be prolonged, or the handspakes must be used by turns.

The next chapter describes how the spanner, when not permanently fixed to a bank, is lashed by its rings to a ladder, to which the patient is fastened; a cord from the limb of the patient is tied to the peg in the spanner, and the pull is exerted. The following chapters describe in detail the dislocations of the different limbs and their treatment. Then Oreibasios goes on:

"49:21. The chest of Nymphodoros

1. The chest of Nymphodoros belongs to the so-called square spanners. 2. It has two sides joined to one another by their ends by means of the so-called cross-pieces; the cross-pieces have the same dimensions as the sides, two palaists (15.4

cm) long and broad, two daktyls (3.8 cm) thick. 3. Since their dimensions are the same, it had to become a chest quite like the so-called square. 4. In the middle of the sides, which are undercut and hollowed out by shallow hollows, there is hidden an axle with a wheel on its middle, and on this wheel there are either on each side iron eyes, two in all, or holes for the tying of ropes, which are fastened in this way; two ropes are by their middles put round the eyes and tied on each side near the holes. 5. There are thus four ends, two of which are passed through the cross-piece in front, which is perforated from the inside out; the other two through the cross-piece in the back. 6. The wheel is engaged by a lentil-shaped screw called "the screw-axle in engagement", whose one end is placed in a hole made in the front cross-piece, the screw-thread engages the wheel; the rest of its length is passed through the hole, and has on its end a handle for turning it, so that the screw-axle by the turning of the handle will turn the wheel; when the wheel is turned, the axle is turned, and when the axle is moved, the outgoing ends of the ropes are drawn in for the stretchings. 7. The chest also has lids to hide the mechanism inside it; it also has four rings nailed to the sides, two above and two below, for lashing the spanner."

Fig. 66 shows my reconstruction of the chest of Nymphodoros. It is a very compact engine: the space between the sides is no more than twice their thickness. The remark that the sides are "undercut and hollowed out by shallow hollows" I take to mean that the ends of the axle are imbedded in the sides, as I have shown it for the end of the screw. The description of the screw is not quite clear; I understand it so that one end is imbedded in the forward cross-piece, while the other end comes out through the back and is provided with a handle.

"49:21:8. This construction is by Aristion, Father of Pasikrates, although the mechanism of the spanner according to Nymphodoros is otherwise; for in the old construction the placing of the screw-axle is not in the cross-pieces, but on the side where are the lids; for there are two iron holders nailed to the sides, with holes in their middles, one of which is under, the other over the axle; both, however, are parallel to part of the wheel. 9. The lower holder has a narrower hole, the upper one a wider hole, so that the screw-axle is held inside between the lids by the holders. 10. The lower lid is closed without difficulty; the upper lid is shut over the projecting, thinner part of the screw-axle, on which the handle is fastened. 11. This lid then either is cut out in the middle, or it is cut in two across, and one part of it stays on immovably, but the other one is put on, with a crescent-shaped cut in the middle of its length, so that when the lid is closed, the crescent-shaped cut takes the projecting part of the screw-axle."

This description of the original construction is quite clear; it also shows why it was found necessary to alter it.

"12. Aristion did not approve of the construction by Nymphodoros, but put in an extra axle with wheels and holes, so that the middle one of the axles, however it was moved, could be made fast and not stirred by the power."

How this was done it not clear; also it was quite unnecessary, for a worm-and-wheel arrangement will stay in any position against any pull on the wheel.

"13. He also moved the rings nearer to the forward cross-piece, so that the lashing of the spanner should not be by where the lids are, but by the forward cross-piece, and at the same time he passed the ends of the ropes out through the lids, two upwards, two downwards."

In the original construction the ropes came out through the cross-pieces, and the spanner was lashed to the ladder with one lid on the ladder, the other, where the screw came out, upward. When Aristion placed the screw in the cross-pieces, he turned the spanner so that it rested on one cross-piece, and the screw came out of the other; then he had to pass out the ropes through the lids.

"14. We approve of the placing of the rings, but we reject that of the second axle as superfluous; for one axle is enough for the purpose, if it is made of strong material. 15. Now that we have described the construction of the chest, we shall next come also to the working of the instrument."

The next chapter explains the use of the "chest" in the resetting operations. The text goes on:

"23. The triple pulley of Apellis or Archimedes

1. First let us bear in mind that neither Apellis nor Archimedes was a doctor, but they were mechanics who invented the instrument, as we learn from history, for hauling ships by pulling the ropes not by hand, but by winches; the doctors of that time reduced the dimensions of the construction and made out of the triple pulley a surgical spanner for resetting dislocations and fractures. 2. It is constructed like this; and on the whole it belongs in kind to the so-called oblong quadrangles; and it is put together in this way. 3. There are two sides, four palaists (31 cm) long, ⟨two palaists (15.4 cm) broad⟩, one daktyl (1.9 cm) thick; these sides are kept together by cross-pieces of two palaists (15.4 cm), one daktyl (1.9 cm) thick. 4. The back cross-piece becomes six daktyls (11.4 cm) broad because of the lids, the forward one two palaists (15.4 cm). 5. According to Pasikrates, in the middle of the sides, which are hollowed out by shallow cuts, there are hidden two axles with wheels near the sides; and each wheel has a hole right through it. These holes are for making fast ropes. This is as follows. 6. Two ropes are taken, with knots on the ends; these ropes are passed through the holes in the foremost axle and are drawn through until the knots come to the holes; and then each rope is passed over its proper wheel and through the holes in the back axle and tied fast. 7. The back axle has in the middle between the wheels a hole; this hole also is for tying a rope. 8. A long rope is taken with a knot at one end; then it is passed through the hole mentioned and pulled, until the knot reaches the hole, next it is wound round the middle of the axle, and then its end is passed through

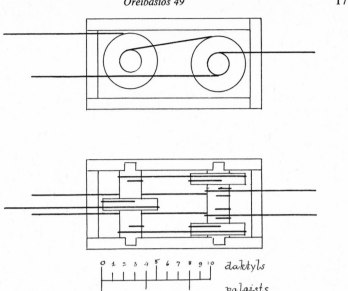

Fig. 67 a. The *trispaston* or triple pulley. This is my reconstruction. See text p. 178 sqq.

the back cross-piece, which has a hole in it. 9. Now what happens? When some-body pulls with his hand and takes up the rope coming out, the back axle is turned; when that is turned, other ends of ropes coming out are pulled in; they are four, two and two. 10. The ropes are tied in like this: two ropes are taken with knots on their ends; these ropes are passed through the two holes in the foremost axle, which are in the middle between the wheels, and are pulled through, until the knots reach the holes; and then the ends of the ropes come out from the inside through the front cross-piece, which has an opening; or a single rope of double length is used, whose ends are passed through the holes in the foremost axle and pulled through, until the middle of the rope comes on the part between the holes. 11. So the ends of the rope come out through the holes in the front cross-piece; and two other ropes are taken, with knots on their ends. 12. These ropes are passed through the two holes in the back axle, being in the space between the wheels, but away from the hole in the middle. 13. These ropes are passed through; then when their knots reach the holes, they are passed round and taken out through the back cross-piece, which has holes for them, so that now in all five ropes come out, two through the front cross-piece, three through the back. 14. When they are drawn by hand by means of the rope through the middle of the back, and the hidden ropes are wound off and on as described, the exposed ends of the ropes will be pulled, and by these ends the straps for the bodies to be stretched will be tightened."

Apellis (or Apellides) seems to be unknown outside this place; Archimedes, ca. 287–212 B.C., is well known, indeed. *Trispaston*, the

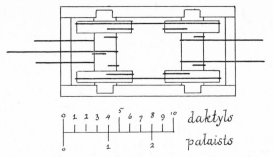

Fig. 67 b. The *trispaston* according to Oreibasios 49:23:1–14. See text p. 178 sqq.

triple pulley, is mentioned by Tzetzes (ca. 1150 A.D.) (128) as the engine with which Archimedes proposed to move the earth; in Vitruvius it is the name of the triple pulley, see p. 143. But here it is clearly the gear used by Vitruvius for one of his cranes, see p. 146 sq, fig. 57, and mentioned by Heron, see p. 83. The description, however, is quite wrong. My reconstruction of the original shape is shown in fig. 67a. All the four ropes for the limbs of the patient have to come from the forward axle; the ropes from the wheel of this axle should go round the back axle itself, not the wheels on it; and the back axle should have only one wheel, in the middle, round which the rope to be pulled by hand should be wound.

The text says only that the ropes from the front wheels are to be tied to the holes in the back axle; but this can mean only the holes in the wheels of that axle, since no other holes have been mentioned, and the wheels are sitting opposite each other.

To suit the dimensions given for the frame I have made the wheels 5 daktyls (10 cm) in diameter, the axles 2 daktyls (4 cm); this gives a ratio of $^2/_5 \times ^2/_5 = ^4/_{25}$, or a little more than 1:6, which should be enough for the purpose.

It is not possible, however, just to correct the text to get the proper construction; in view of the following, we must assume that the inventors were so successful in hiding the mechanism from their patients (and competitors?), that Pasikrates did not know how to assemble the spanner.

Fig. 67 b shows how it looked according to the text, and it is evident that it will not work: there is no gear at all. The hand pulling on the long rope from the middle of the back axle has to exert a pull equal to that of the four ropes for the patient; the wheels transmit the power in the ratio 1:1.

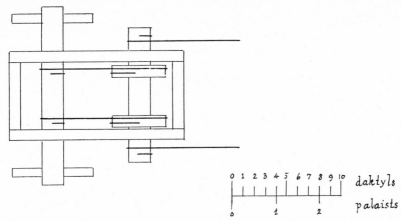

Fig. 67c. The *trispaston* as modified by Pasikrates, from Oreibasios 49:23:15–18. See text p. 181 sq.

"15. Pasikrates criticized this construction and denounced the instrument as unpractical; for the whole effect of the instrument is a movement when the back rope is pulled by hand; but the hand is not strong enough in the resettings to bear so much power, especially in big joints and strong bodies; for this reason he changed the instrument and made the two hidden axles to project outside, making the front axle smaller in the round projections, but the back axle larger and with greater projections. 16. And on the front axle he fixed pegs in the round projections, but on the back axle he put handles or bars. 17. Having tied the axles by two hidden pegs, he moved the instrument for resetting in this way. 18. The straps from the bodies to be stretched he put round the visible pegs on the front axle, so that the stretchings took place by the turning of the back axle and by the front axle being turned by the ropes round it."

The text of v. 17 is corrupt. One MS has: δυσὶ κρυπτοῖς δακτύλοις, "with two hidden fingers"; the other MS has δυσι τοις δακτύλοις, "with the two fingers". This was corrected in the old edition into δυσεκρίπτως τοῖς δακτύλοις, "hard to tear out, with the fingers"; but by Ræder into δυσὶ κρυπτοῖς τύλοις, "by two hidden pegs". I take this to mean that Pasikrates tied the ropes from the wheels of the front axle to two pegs on the back axle, and so gained a gear of 5:2 for his back axle.

Fig. 67c shows my reconstruction of the *trispaston* of Pasikrates.

"19. But Aristion, the son of Pasikrates, objected that his father did not understand the original construction of the engine; for in the original construction of the instrument, he says, the axles did not move in bearings in the sides, but on pivots fixed to the sides, and they had holes like door-sockets, as we can see it done in the water-lifting engines, which turn easily by this construction. 20. But the wheels are not hollow, but outstanding. 21. But since they are turned by sockets round pivots, and the wheels are standing out, and the axles are moving very easily, the stretchings will be unhampered, even if the rope is pulled by hand; and it was also for this reason that the instrument was called a triple pulley, because there are three ropes in action, one outside, two hidden."

It seems entire likely that the sides of one daktyl only, not quite 2 cm, were not thick enough for a concealed bearing; the sides of the chest of Nymphodoros were two daktyls, 3.8 cm, thick for just this purpose. So the construction with fixed pivots going into the axles is probably correct. In the following sentence the text is not in order. The MSS have κοιλότητας ἔχοντας ἑλικοειδεῖς, "(the pivots) having screw-shaped hollows"; which is corrected by the old edition into κοιλότητα ἔχοντες ὁλμισκοειδῆ, "(the axles) having a door-socket-like hollow". Though Ræder accepts the text of the MSS, I prefer the correction, the more so since the word "door-socket" is repeated below.

In the description of the water-snail in Vitruvius, see p. 152 sq, the snail turns on pivots moving in sockets fixed to the posts; but it is quite possible that the other construction, with fixed pivots and bearings in the snail, can have been in use also.

Verse 20 has puzzled Bernhard Faust very much (31). He takes it to mean that Aristion made the wheels larger, so that they came out above the sides, but admits that κοῖλος, "hollow" does not in itself mean "small", but here just has to have the opposite sense of ὑπερέχων "standing out" and, later, μετέωρος, "high". But the text does not state that Aristion built any spanner at all; he seems only to have made some observations on the construction of the original *trispastos*. His remark may mean that the place where the rope went round the axle, which was really a drum, was not a hollow in the axle, but a wheel with a greater diameter; and when we take this together with the remark on the name of the *trispastos* coming from the three ropes, two inside, one outside, we may be allowed to conclude that he had understood the original construction, as shown by me in fig. 67a, only that his description has not reached us in a very clear form. Faust gives the same construction, in his fig. XI, *Organum non traditum* (32), but this, he says, though without doubt a good engine, is invented by himself and not mentioned at all by Heliodoros. I venture to think that it is meant by Aristion, but I admit that it was not understood by Heliodoros, as will be seen in the following.

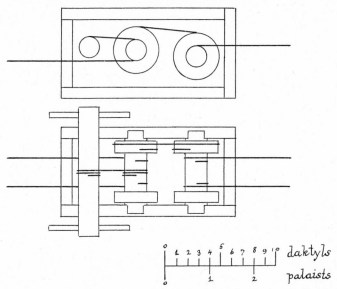

Fig. 67 d. The *trispaston* as modified by Heliodoros, from Oreibasios 49:23:22–27.
See text p. 183 sq.

"22. These are his arguments; but what Pasikrates said is the truth: the hand is not strong enough to reset properly by pulling a rope, though it may perhaps move the instrument for a theoretical demonstration, but the power for resetting will not come from the hand; and for this reason it has seemed good to us, leaving things as they have been described in the old construction, to add a third, projecting axle to the instrument, so that the back axle now becomes the middle one. 23. The back axle should have a hole, and in the projecting, round ends either handspakes or cranks or handles; the end of the middle rope in the back, after it has gone round the axle, goes through the hole in the exposed axle and is tied. 24. When this has been done, then by the turning of the back axle, that is, the exposed axle, as the rope is wound over on to the exposed axle, the middle axle is moved; and as that is turned, also the front axle is moved; by the turning of these three axles the exposed ends of the ropes are pulled in, to which are tied the straps from the bodies to be stretched. 25. The spanner also has lids like the chest to hide the mechanism; it also has rings on the sides for lashing. 26. That is the whole construction of the triple pulley; the resettings are the same as those explained about the chest; for the engines differ, in fact, but the ropes are pulled in in the same way, with the straps knotted to the ropes. 27. So we have finished the construction of the triple pulley."

With Heliodoros we return to the construction denounced by Pasikrates; but Heliodoros prefers to have his mechanism hidden, and so

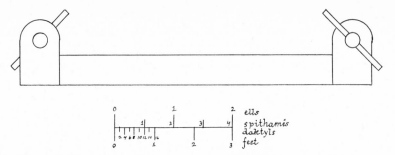

Fig. 68. A diagram of the bank of Hippokrates, from Oreibasios 49:27. See text p. 184 sq.

he just adds a third axle. In fig. 67 d I have given a diagram of the construction; to find room for the third axle it would be necessary either to make the sides longer, or to move the two original axles together and reduce the diameters of the wheels. This could easily be done, since the wheels, as explained above, do not serve as reducing gear at all. For my diagram I have used the latter method.

The following chapter describes the engine of Tekton; this last word is now taken to be a proper name, while the older editions regarded it as a noun: the engine of the carpenter. The power here is an axle turned by handspakes; what is new is that the ropes draw a "tortoise" and are not fastened to the patient himself.

> "27. From the works of Rufus. The bank of Hippokrates
>
> The admirable Hippokrates has called this instrument "log", in many of his works; in some "raft" (or "lath"); those after him have called it "bank", and they have put legs under it as an instrument and have used it as a bank. 2. Its construction is as follows: a log of wood, six ells (2.78 m) long, two ells (0.93 m) broad, about one spithame (23 cm) thick. 3. This piece of wood has fastened on the end of the plank lying down other pieces of wood, one foot (30.8 cm) long, four in number, two and two, rounded at the top. 4. These boards Hippokrates called "posts"; in these posts, in round holes going right through their sides, projecting axles were placed, with pegs in their middle and with handles on the round, projecting ends for turning."

The further details of this instrument are of no interest here.

Fig. 68 is a diagram made in accordance with the text.

Rufus is a well-known physician, who lived in the 1. century A.D.; but several authors ascribe this chapter not to him, but to Heliodoros. As for Hippokrates, he lived about 420 B.C.; the "bank" is described in his works (71) and discussed in the preface; the shape is the same.

This is obviously the original of the other engines; for its use it was necessary to have helpers posted at the handles of the axles all the time, under the supervision of the surgeon. We can take it that for a stationary instrument the same dimensions were used, more or less; for transportable instruments the spanners were used together with a ladder procured on the spot.

Engines of War

Of all the technical writings of Antiquity those on the engines of war have received by far the best treatment. The texts have been edited and translated; the figures have been reproduced and interpreted; the catapults have been reconstructed and tried (49, 91, 107, 114). So I can confine myself to a short survey of the more important details.

The writings are divided into two groups, the *belopoiics*, describing catapults, and the *poliorcetics*, dealing with siege-towers, battering-rams and the like. Biton writes on both subjects; but, as I have said p. 11, his works are of no use to us at all.

The Belopoiics

The ancient artillery was built on the bow as a model. The long-bow was drawn by hand; in the cross-bow some extra strength could be used. Heron describes such a weapon by the name of *gastraphetês*, the "stomach-bow". The bow was fixed to a stock; a board sliding in a dove-tail groove projected beyond the bow. The archer, leaning his whole weight against the stock, which was curved to fit his stomach, drove this slider into the stock; a hook on the slider caught the bow-string, and two pawls sliding over racks held the slider when the bow was spanned. An arrow was placed before the string, and after sighting the archer pulled a trigger for his shot. Then the slider was slid forwards to catch the string once more, and the bow could be spanned again.

This arrangement was enlarged and used for the catapults, which were standing on the ground. There were two types; a smaller one was for shooting arrows; here the stock was mounted on a tripod on two axles, one horizontal, one vertical, so that it could be sighted by hand. In the larger type the weapon was fixed to the stand, so that the whole thing had to be turned for sighting; but then it was used for hurling stones and bolts; its target was not men, but the wall.

In stead of the elastic bow, the catapults had two strong arms of hard wood; the elasticity was provided by a long rope plaited of sinews. This was passed in many turns round two bolts placed across holes in a strong frame, forming thus a bundle into which the end of the arm was thrust.

The ancient authors knew well enough that the strength of the cata-

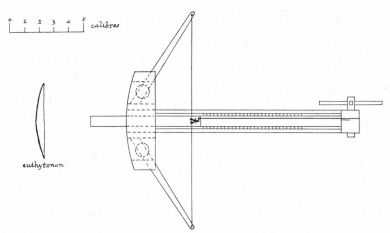

Fig. 69. A diagram of the arrow catapult (*euthytonon*). See text p. 187 sq.

pult depended on the size of this spanner, that is of the hole in the *peritrete*, as the ends of the frame were called. They computed the diameter of the hole from the length of the arrow or the weight of the stone, and used this calibre as a module for all the dimensions of the catapult.

Like the stomach-bow the catapult had a slider projecting forwards; a hook on its inner end caught the bow-string. It was then pulled back by means of a winch at the inner end of the stock; in the larger catapults pulleys were used to increase the power of the winch. The slider was held by pawls sliding over two racks; when the arrow or stone had been put into its place, a trigger was pulled and the weapon discharged. Then the slider was pushed forwards to catch the bow-string once more.

The smaller catapult, shooting arrows, was called *euthytonon;* the larger one, hurling stones, was called *palintonon.*

Fig. 69 shows a diagram of an *euthytonon* with the arms going through the bundles of sinews and holding the string. The bundles are held by two boards with four cross-pieces. The slider is shown with the rope to the winch, and the two racks are indicated. The stock in which the slider moves was called the pipe; it was a solid board with an undercut groove for the slider.

Fig. 70 shows a diagram of a *palintonon*. Here the sinews are held in two separate frames kept together by a frame above and below. The stock, which here is called the ladder, consists of two parallel planks with cross pieces at intervals.

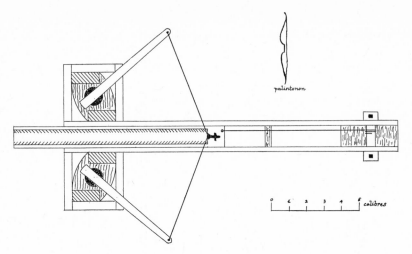

Fig. 70. A diagram of the stone catapult (*palintonon*). See text p. 187 sq.

The words *euthytonon* and *palintonon* mean two types of bow; the *euthytonon*, the "straight-bent", is the long-bow showing a single curve; the *palintonon*, the "backwards-bent", is the cupid's bow with a straight middle and two arms showing double curves. The application of these terms to the catapults has puzzled the modern authors; Diels indeed gives up any attempt to explain it (13).

I think that the difference is found in the shape of the front of the catapult. In the reconstructions of the *euthytonon* by Schramm (116) the curved side of the *peritrete*, the board with the holes, is turned towards the back; but in the MS drawing reproduced in the edition of Heron's Belopoiica (49) it seems to me evident that it was turned forwards, since the arms are shown coming out from the flat side. If a shield was put on to follow this curve, we should have a picture of the straight bow; see fig. 69.

In the *palintonon* the two spanner frames were not square, but rhomboid in shape. If we imagine shields placed on both, the front may have suggested a cupid's bow; see fig. 70.

These types have been described almost in the same fashion by Philon (250 B.C.) (91), Vitruvius (25 B.C.) (135) and Heron (62 A.D.), and they may be regarded as the standard artillery of Greek and Roman Antiquity.

Later on an one-armed *ballista*, the *onager*, came into use (1, 124). The arm moved in a vertical plane and hurled a stone from a sling. The moving power was still a rope of sinews.

Philon, however, is not content with the ordinary catapults and describes several improvements. The weak point of the catapult was the sinew-rope; it changed its tension with the humidity of the air; it had to be loosened, when the catapult was not in use, and tightened again; the two bundles had to have exactly the same tension, or the catapult would not shoot straight.

The bolts round which the rope was wound were held by bronze bushes going partly into the holes in the peritrete; the friction of bronze against wood was enough to hold them from turning; they were turned by means of a long key. In an ancient catapult discovered at Ampurias in Spain in 1912 (115), the bushes were placed on rings of bronze and had to be kept from turning by pins through holes. In the rings were 16 holes, equally spaced; in the feet of the bushes were 6 holes, in groups of three, spaced at $1/_{24}$ of the circumference. This meant that the adjustment could be made by steps of 7°30′, and this is the first example of the differential principle now extensively used in the vernier of instruments of precision. This catapult is dated at 150 B.C., that is 100 years later than Philon.

Philon first describes a way of altering the tension of the sinews by replacing the bolts by wedges (92, 117). This is technically a fine solution, since the extra twisting of the sinews would tend to destroy their elasticity little by little.

Next he tries to replace the sinews by springs made from hammered bronce-plates (93, 118).

Finally he tries compressed air: the inner ends of the arms press on two pistons to compress the air in two cylinders.

Schramm regards this last model as a theoretical invention rather than an actual weapon (121), and he could not make it work, partly because it loses pressure, if it is not discharged at once, but mostly because it was impossible, even by using an air-pump, of which Philon says nothing, to get the same power on both arms.

The wedge-spanner is Philon's own invention; the spring-spanner he ascribes to Ktesibios, but the construction was made and tried by himself. The air-spanner also is an invention by Ktesibios, and Schramm is right in his interpretation of the text: Philon is not describing a catapult made by himself, but is just giving an account of Ktesibios's own description.

In between he describes a wonderful invention by one Dionysios of Alexandria, a veritable machine gun for shooting arrows (94, 119). The idea was that the men had only to turn the winch forwards and back, and then the arrows would come out just as fast as they could work the handles. The catapult had to be sighted once for all and fixed in this position. How this was done Philon, who saw the thing itself, cannot tell; he merely noticed that the man had to press down hard on a handle. The lock probably held some sort of wedge.

The slider was brought back and pushed forward by a pin carried by an endless chain running over two pentagonal wheels, one at each end of the pipe. The claw was made to grip the string by itself, and was then automatically locked, until the slider had been brought back and an arrow had been dropped before the string; then the string was released automatically, the arrow went away, and the slider was brought forward once more.

The arrows were kept in a container above the pipe, a cylinder with a groove to take just one arrow at a time formed its bottom; this cylinder was turned by an arm on the chain engaging a curved furrow on its outside.

All this is very ingenious, but Philon does not believe in shooting out a lot of arrows without sighting each shot; it means just to present them to the enemy. They were not notched, because they fell down before the string as best they could; but indeed, he adds ironically, it is a hard and time-consuming task to notch an arrow!

Schramm in his reconstruction found that the five-sided wheels would not pull the chain at all; to try the other working parts he substituted bicycle chains, and then found that the catapult shot well and with great precision.

R. Schneider has advanced the hypothesis (112, 113) that the *scorpio* used by Caesar at Avaricum was such a repeating catapult. Schramm rejects the idea (122), but Fr. Lammert takes it up again (78). In a paper read in Barcelona in 1959 (30) I have tried to show that there is no evidence at all for this supposition.

In view of the fact that none of the later authors mentions the inventions described by Philon, I hold that we may regard them all as clever inventions, indeed, but premature: they came to nothing.

Siege engines

Not even the strongest catapults were able by themselves to batter down the walls of a well fortified town. It was necessary for the besiegers to operate directly on the wall, and during this operation they had to be protected from the bolts and arrows of the garrison.

This was done by means of a solid roof, a "tortoise", which was wheeled forward against the wall. Under this shield the besiegers could dig down under the wall or break it down with a battering-ram or prepare to scale it by ladders.

The tortoise was pushed forward by men marching inside it; in Biton it seems that a tread-mill was used (7); but I cannot use Biton for evidence of anything.

The ram was a long, heavy piece of timber with a ram's head of bronze, hanging in ropes, and swung against the wall. It might also be provided with a hook for tearing down, or it might be turned, by means of a rope laid round it, to drill holes in the bricks (108). This was an enlargement of the hand-drill, turned by a string held in a bow, an instrument of very great age. One such wall-drill was slid along a row of rollers (110).

As for scaling ladders, they might be set up by means of winches; in Biton (8) a scaling-ladder with a counterpoise is set up by means of a screw; but here once more the whole chapter bristles with difficulties, and so it is no use for us at all.

In Apollodoros, ab. 120 A.D., we find a bucket-chain (109) used for lifting boiling water or pitch to pour over the defenders of the wall; in Athenaios the Mechanic, about 27 A.D., there is a devise for steering a tortoise (111): the axle of the two front wheels can be made to turn, for it is held by a vertical axle, which is turned by a rope over a drum inside the tortoise.

Sundries

With the belopoiics and the poliorcetics we have finished with the general works on mechanical technology; but from other technical works we can still gather bits of information about the way in which some mechanical problems were solved.

Ktesibios was one of the great inventors; but his works have come down to us only through extracts and quotations by later writers. One of his most prominent inventions was the water-clock, in which a container was filled with water at a constant rate; to measure the hours a float was placed in the container, and the movement of the float was used to indicate the time of the day. Here are the words of Vitruvius, 9:8:5:

> "On it (the float) a rod is placed ⟨in conjunction with⟩ a turning wheel. They are provided with equally spaced teeth, which teeth impinging on each other cause proper turnings and movements. Also other rods and other wheels, with teeth after the same fashion, driven by this single movement by their turning cause effects and varieties of movements, by which puppets are moved, cones are turned, pebbles and eggs are dropped, horns are sounded, and other by-plays."

The by-plays, however, "which are not for necessity, but for the enjoyment of pleasures", Vitruvius refuses to describe further; he refers us to Ktesibios's own works, which unfortunately are lost (132).

Still, we learn from this place that Ktesibios used rack-and-cogwheel arrangements, and that this probably is the first time they were used, since Vitruvius, quoting Ktesibios himself, gives a complete description of the instrument: "provided with equally spaced teeth". Also it would seem that no pointer moving across a scale was used; that came later. This first clock was a great show: the puppets came out, the cones, half white and half black, were turned to show the hour, pebbles or balls were dropped into a bronze basin, to count the hours, and horns were sounded, probably at midday. This clock is sometimes reconstructed with an hour hand on the first axle, indicating the hours on a circular dial; but of this there is no trace in the text, and it is in itself quite improbable. The clock had to be "wound" every day, that is, the container had to be emptied, and the float had to be let down to the bottom. Since the movement could not be continuous, there was no need for a circular dial; and indeed all the later clocks, except one, the anaphoric clock, have pointers travelling over straight lines—up or down or across.

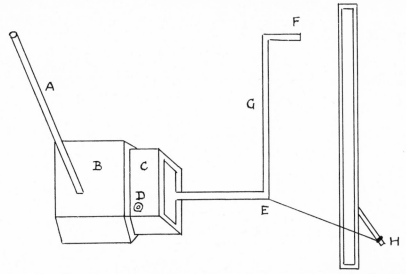

Fig. 71 is taken from Codex Hauniensis Thott 215; it shows Heron's key for his water-organ. See text p. 193 sq.

The difficulty with the water-clock was that it had to show hours of different length, since the hours of the day were one twelfth of the time from sunrise to sunset, while the watches of the night were one twelfth of the time from sunset to sunrise. How this difficulty was met by the construction of an adjustable scale and, later, an adjustable flow of water, has been described by me in another work (21).

As for the anaphoric clock (22), it consisted of a map of the sky, complete with constellations and an adjustable sun; this was turned by a chain tied by one end to the float, going round the axle, and with a counterpoise in the other end. But even in this case the movement was not continuous; the disk had to be turned back every morning to its original position. The anaphoric clock can with great probability be ascribed to the astronomer Hipparchos, who lived 190 — 120 B.C. (25).

Another invention by Ktesibios was the water organ, for which he had to construct a keyboard. We have two descriptions of the keyboard: one in Vitruvius (133), probably taken from Ktesibios himself, and another in Heron, illustrated, and describing the actual instrument (61).

Heron's description is quite clear. The wind was supplied by pumps; a row of pipes sat on a channel into which the air was pressed. For each pipe there was a valve consisting of a square chamber closed by a square slider made of wood. If the slider was pushed in, a hole in it connected the pipe with the channel below.

In Heron the slider is called πῶμα, "a lid". It is moved by means of a key, ἀγκονίσκος τρίκωλος, "a small, three-armed elbow", which pushes it in, while a slip of horn acts as a spring to pull it back again. Fig. 71 is taken from a MS of the Pneumatics; I have changed the letters for ease of reference. A is the pipe, B is the chamber, C the solid slider, D the hole. EF is the "elbow" with a pivot at G; H is the spring, fastened to a board parallel to the front of the organ.

In Vitruvius matters are not quite so plain (134). There are several channels or registers, each closed by a separate valve. The top of a channel is called *canon*, a ruler, with holes corresponding to the holes in a *tabula* or πίναξ, a board, on which the pipes are sitting. In between is a set of square sticks, *regulae* or *plinthides,* the sliders. The Greek word *plinthis* means a brick or any other square object. None of the Greek words, κανών, πίναξ, πλινθίς, is used by Heron in this connexion. No individual chambers for the pipes are mentioned; it looks as if the sliders, which were well oiled, simply slid along each other; they must have been rather long, since each served one pipe in every channel.

The text now runs: *haec regulae habent ferrea choragia fixa et iuncta cum pinnis, quarum pinnarum tactus motiones efficit regularum continenter.* "These rulers have iron *choragia* fixed and connected with feathers, and the touch on these feathers cause continuously movements of the rulers". "Feather" may mean not only a feather or quill, but also any thin, flat thing, as the fins of a fish or the paddles of a water-wheel. Here it means the keys of the keyboard, as we find later on: "So when the feathers, touched by the hands, continuously push and pull the rulers, now opening, now closing the holes in turn ..." But then they cannot have looked like Heron's elbows, or Vitruvius, who is always strong on details, would have described them more fully.

The word *choragium* in Latin (40) means 1) the equipment for producing a theatre play (decorations, machinery, furniture, dresses). 2) the whole apparatus of the imperial theatre. 3) a great display. In Greek the word χοράγιον means: 1) a school for training a chorus. 2) supply for an army; maintenance. 3) stage building in a theatre.

The Latin dictionary adds 4) (technical word) a spring (Vitruvius 10:8:4). In an earlier work I have accepted this interpretation, but I cannot do so any more. Since it is impossible to connect the sense

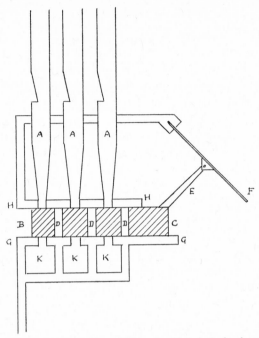

Fig. 72 is a diagram showing my interpretation of Vitruvius 10:8:3–5, the description
of Ktesibios's keyboard for his water-organ. See text p. 194 sqq.

"spring" or any small object with any other sense of the word in two
languages, it seems reasonable to assume that it is misspelt. Then the
word κοράκιον, *coracium*, suggests itself. It is a diminutive of κόραξ,
"a raven", which means also a raven's beak or any thing resembling it:
a pawl, any thing hooked or pointed like a raven's beak; and it is just
the sort of thing that would be made of iron. On the other hand an
iron spring at the time of Ktesibios is very improbable; we see from
Philon that Ktesibios used bronze springs for his catapult, not steel.

Further, we cannot get a clear idea of the keyboard in Vitruvius if
we translate: "these rulers have iron springs fastened and connected
with flat keys", for the springs must be fastened to the frame to be of
any use, and the rulers have to be connected with the keys, as in Heron.
But if we take *choragia* to be *coracia*, we get: "these rulers have fixed on
them iron pegs, which are connected with thin, flat boards …" and the
construction becomes clear: the "feathers" were boards thin enough to
serve as springs; the "three-armed elbows" are a later improvement.

Fig. 72 is a diagram to show how I understand the construction. A A A are three pipes; B is the space between the *canones*, G G, and the *tabulae*, H H; C is the slider, *regula*, and D D D are the holes in it. E is the iron pin, *coracium*, and F the key, *pinna*. K K K are three air-channels.

In 1948 I held (19) that Vitruvius was writing from actual experience, because he adds (134):

> "I have done my best so that a difficult matter should be set forth clearly in writing, but that is not an easy way, and it is not given to everybody to understand it except those who have experience in these sorts of things. But he who has understood little from the writings, when he comes to know the thing itself, will assuredly find everything put together in an interesting and clever way."

I do not now think that this must mean that Vitruvius has not taken his description from Ktesibios. But my sympathy goes out to the practical man, who has laboriously striven, "with true sweat of soul", to express himself in words, and who now advises us to go and look at the thing itself, and to admire it, as he does.

From Philon's Pneumatics (96) there is not much to be gleaned; there are some puppets moved by floats by means of levers, but the most interesting thing is an automaton serving guests with water for washing hands (97). There is a spout, and above it a hand holding a ball of pumice stone, the substitute, at that time, for soap. When the guest takes this ball, the hand vanishes and water begins to flow; the water stops after a time and the hand reappears with another ball of pumice stone for the next guest. The description is not quite clear, but we can see one mechanical detail: the hand, released from the weight of the stone, procures by its own movement another stone which brings it back again. This principle was used later on in a very ingenious water-clock (137), which however belongs to a much later period than the one with which we are dealing.

In Heron's Pneumatics (56) we find two toothed wheels at right angles to turn a bird on the top of a casket (65), and a rack-and-cog-wheel arrangement for a self-snuffing lamp (60). A rather ingenious contrivance (66) lets us pass a knife through the neck of an animal, as if to cut off its head; but the head stays on, and the animal will drink water both before and after being beheaded. The head is held by a wheel with dove-tailed cross-section; but the wheel consists only of three sectors of about one sixth each of the whole circumference. One sector holds the head, while the other two are inside the body. The knife passing through turns the wheel, which never lets go of its hold. The pipe for the water is opened for the knife to pass and closed again by means of sectors of wheels operating two racks.

In Heron's Automatic Theatre (45) we see how much could be done with the mechanical means of the time. There are two different constructions; one is a small stage which all by itself comes into view, presents a puppet-show, and then retires again. The other is a stage standing still, but presenting, all by itself, a play in many acts.

In both cases the moving force is a heavy weight fitting into a container full of millet or mustard seeds; the seeds run out through a narrow hole, the weight comes down at a determined rate, and it turns an axle from which it is suspended by a cord. All the movements are taken from this axle by means of strings. A puppet or any other thing is turned by a string going round a drum; if it has to turn back, the string is passed over a peg in the drum and wound round the other way. If it has to move, and stop, and move again, there is a length of slack string between two windings; this slack is stuck on the drum with wax, so that it will not hang down and get caught in the other machinery. If a thing has to happen only once, as a back cloth being dropped, it may be worked by a separate weight which is released by a string pulling out a pin. The moving stage runs in and out on three wheels; it may be moved back and forward by another set of wheels that are lowered and lifted by a screw-furrow engaged by a peg. A movement of the arm of a puppet, e.g. hammering, is produced by pins on a wheel acting on the short end of a lever.

The most interesting feature of all this is the entire absense of cog-wheels. Drums and strings, strings and drums—these are the only mechanical implements which Heron trusted to do his work. But with these limited means he produces a great variety of effects.

W. Schmidt, who edited the Automatic Theatre, has shown how it is possible to make the bacchantes that dance round a temple spin round also, by means of wheels turned by friction (46, 106). There is not the slightest indication of such a thing in Heron (47). He describes how to make a ring turn round the temple, by means of strings, and then adds: "for the bacchantes are to stand on this ring". That is all.

In Heron's Dioptra (51) we find an instrument of a very high quality; on the other hand there is no indication that it has ever existed in more than one copy.

It was a surveyor's instrument, with a theodolite and a water-level that could be fitted on the same foot (27).

The foot itself, probably a tripod or table of wood, is not described; the rest of the instrument was made mostly of bronze. There was a holder like a column carrying a round, horizontal plate fixed round the foot of a strong, vertical pivot. Round this pivot turned a toothed wheel, which was engaged with a screw mounted on brackets on the plate. This screw had its furrow cut away by a longitudinal groove as broad as the wheel was thick. The wheel could turn freely when the groove was opposite it; but it could be locked in any position by a slight turn of the screw. On this holder could be mounted either the theodolite or the water-level, for they were each built on a hollow column that fitted the pivot and which had on the underside three pins going into holes in the toothed wheel. In the theodolite this column ended in a doric capital, which carried a half-circle of bronze turning between two flat rulers. This half-circle was toothed, and a screw between the rulers engaged it. On top of this vertical half-circle was fixed a full circle, which carried the sighting apparatus, an alhidade with a pointer at each end. On the horizontal disk two lines were scribed at right angles, one coinciding with the half-circle below.

The water-level consisted also of a hollow column with three pins; it carried a long horizontal rod which was hollowed out to take a bronze tube. At either end this tube was turned up to take a small tube of glass. When water was poured in, the surfaces of the water in the two glass tubes determined a horizontal line. Round each of the tubes was set up a frame along which a bronze plate could slide up and down, touching the glass. These two plates held slits for sighting; when these slits were adjusted opposite the level of the water in the two tubes, a horizontal line was determined. The bronze plates were steered by screws going through the rod; for these thin bronze screws no female screws could be made; they passed through a smooth hole, where a pin from the side engaged the screw-thread.

For staff Heron used a post with a big shield, half white, half black, sliding up and down a dove-tailed groove and held in position by a cord.

The whole instrument was probably invented by Heron himself; it is very ingenious and certainly quite effective, but no record is found of its having survived its author. I take it that it was too expensive to make.

Survey of the results

So far I have let the old authors speak for themselves; now let us try to find out how much was theory only and how much was actual practice. Here it is Heron who makes us doubt; Vitruvius and Oreibasios may be trusted to give us practice only. We can take the five powers in their proper order.

The winch

The winch or capstan was used extensively, as seen from Vitruvius and Oreibasios, also from Cato major (11), who describes wine- and oil-presses. For confirmation we have a wall painting from Pompeji, showing a wine press (80), and three reliefs, of which one shows a press (16), while the other two (10, 37, 70, 74) show tread-wheels for hoisting stones for buildings.

In cranes and the like the winch was combined with the pulley, which gave it extra power; but it was possible also to gear the winch itself; see the crane in Vitruvius, p. 146, and fig. 57, and the *trispaston* of Oreibasios, p. 179, fig. 67a. Heron uses this device in his automatic theatre (48); but the most interesting place is the Mechanics 2:21, see p. 83. Here he describes in detail how to lift 1000 talents with a power of five talents only by means of toothed wheels; then he adds, as an afterthought, that if we do not want to use toothed wheels, we can put in ropes instead. And then he tells us to put the axles and wheels into solid posts and set them up in a firm piece of ground. This seems to indicate that the arrangement with the toothed wheels was not practicable at all; if we wanted a gear, we had better use ropes. This is confirmed by the fact that neither Vitruvius nor Oreibasios uses cog-wheels engaging each other for any of their engines for hoisting or pulling. We may note here that endless chains and ropes are not used; one end is fixed on the axle, the other on the wheel.

In the catapults also a winch was used, in the greater ones helped by pulleys; see p. 187. In the automatic catapult, see p. 190, an endless chain of blocks running over five-sided wheels was used, but this construction never came off, and Schramm could not make it work (120).

Biton seems to indicate (7) that the siege tower of Poseidonios was moved forward by some sort of tread-mill, and Schramm's reconstruction shows endless ropes for transmitting the power. The whole place, as usually in Biton, is extremely doubtful; but we can be sure, I think, that the transmission can only have been made by single ropes. Endless ropes or chains or belts are known only from bucket chains in Vitruvius, see p. 151, or the poliorcetics, see p. 191; but here they are driven only, they do not drive anything.

Toothed wheels

Since Heron obviously takes toothed wheels to belong theoretically with the winch, we may as well here go into the whole question of cog-wheels in Antiquity.

There are four different ways to use cog-wheels for transmission: parallel wheels engaging each other; wheels at right angles engaging each other; a wheel engaging a rack; a screw engaging a wheel: the endless screw.

Parallel wheels engaging each other, which to us is the most obvious way of using toothed wheels, has the draw-back that unless the teeth have a definite and not easily found shape, the friction becomes very high, or the gear will not work at all. Till Ole Rømer, in 1675, calculated the proper shape (73), the cog-wheels had to be made by trial and error, and their working was rather uncertain.

In the more careful MS figures the teeth are shown as equilateral triangles, fig. 5, 62a, 63a; elsewhere they are just a signature, fig. 6, 7, 18a, b, 28a, b, c, 32. In the latter there is a tendency to make the teeth sloping; in fig. 29a, from MS L, this is so pronounced that Carra de Vaux and Nix have copied it in their figure, see fig. 63c. But the figure from MS B, fig. 29c, shows the teeth far more symmetrical; and in the figure from MS L, fig. 29a, the large wheel in the middle shows the lower teeth either symmetrical or pointing the opposite way, in relation to the wheel, of the upper teeth. On redrawing the figures I found that when I was drawing teeth from left to right, they had a tendency to slope and point to the right, and that this tendency had also troubled the ancient scribes. See fig. 6, 7, 18a, 18b, where the lower teeth were probably drawn from right to left, 28b, right to left on lower right quarter of wheel, 29c, 32, right to left on lower right quarter. So I take it that the almost consistent slope of the teeth in fig. 29a is due to an exaggeration by some scribe of a tendency found in his source.

Only one ancient instrument with gear wheels has come to light, the

Antikythera instrument, which was fished up from a ship lost off the island of Antikythera (100). It dates from the second century B.C. and consists of a great number of gear-wheels of brass, to show the movements of the planets. All the wheels have teeth of the same shape: equilateral triangles. There is no doubt that it must have worked when it was in use; but the shape of the teeth is far from ideal, and they can work only because they have very little work to do.

F. M. Feldhaus has discussed the question of cog-wheels in Antiquity (33). He quotes the Mechanical Problems, ch. 1, as proof that cog-wheels were known to Aristoteles; but, as I have shown on p. 13, there is no need to assume gear-wheels in this place. Next he mentions ch. 14: "denn dort sind Walzen besprochen, an denen Vorragungen von Holz sitzen". This must be a slip of the pen, for ch. 14 deals with the breaking of wooden sticks over the knee. Drums are mentioned in ch. 13, see p. 14, where we learn that the thinner drum is easier to turn than a thicker one, scilicet with the same handle; but no teeth are mentioned at all.

But then we do not find any parallel gear-wheels till we come to Heron about 60 A.D. In his Mechanics 2:21 he describes how to lift a burden of 1000 talents with a power of 5 talents by means of gear-wheels; see p. 82 sqq. and fig. 29. But this is evidently a theoretical example only, for he says that if we prefer to use ropes and smooth drums, we can use the same dimensions, and we must then set up the axles in strong posts and place the engine on a solid piece of ground. He hasn't even bothered to put the gear-wheels into bearings: they are theory, pure and simple.

It is otherwise with his Barulkos, see p. 22 sqq. and fig. 5, 6. Here he begins with a framework like a chest and puts in the axles. He explains that if the pivots turn smoothly in their bearings, and the teeth work together without friction, the burden of 1000 talents and the power of 5 talents are in equilibrium, and if we add just one mina, half a kilogram, at either end, this end will come down. But what he does add is an endless screw, which gives him a gear ratio of about 1:25, which he does not compute, and then the workman or slave should certainly be able to overcome the friction from the teeth. But the Barulkos remains a demonstration of a theory; there is no evidence of its use for practical purposes. Neither Vitruvius nor Oreibasios uses parallel gear-wheels for any purpose at all.

Turning to the toothed wheel engaging a rack, we find it described by Vitruvius as part of the water-clock invented by Ktesibios, see p. 192, which would put it about 280 B.C. But here as elsewhere in Ktesibios it was a premature invention (20). No racks and cog-wheels are found in the later clocks; the *parerga* are worked by levers and strings. In the anaphoric clock the rack on the float is superseded by a chain going round the axle, with a counterweight. No racks are found till we come to Heron, who uses them for his pantograph, see p. 33 and fig. 8, and in two pneumatic toys: the self-snuffing lamp (60) and the ox that is beheaded (66). Vitruvius does not use the rack himself, nor does Oreibasios.

Next we come to the endless screw, the combination of a screw and a toothed wheel. This was invented by Archimedes, say about 250 B.C. (28). That he used this superlative power in his war engines is almost certain; but also that its use was not continued: Vitruvius does not mention it among his cranes. Heron, on the other hand, is strong on endless screws, both for his hodometer, see p. 160 and fig. 62a, and for his dioptra, see p. 197. He gives the theory of it, see p. 59 and fig. 18, 28, and teaches us how to make it, see p. 43 and fig. 11; but he does not show us any large model in actual use. In the barulkos, see p. 26, indeed an endless screw is used, but it is quite probable that this engine is more theory than practice, see p. 201.

In Oreibasios, however, we find the endless screw used in the chest of Nymphodoros, see p. 176 and fig. 66. Vitruvius mentions a Nymphodoros who wrote about machinery (130); this would date him before 25 B.C. In cranes for practical purposes the construction was not profitable, because it takes just as much time to wind it back again as it takes to wind it up; in the surgeons' tool this did not matter, since it was used only occasionally and for very short pulls.

The first mention of toothed wheels engaging each other at right angles comes from Vitruvius, where he describes the water-wheel that drives a cornmill, see p. 151. The water-wheel turns a horizontal shaft which carries a toothed wheel; this engages a horizontal toothed wheel on a vertical shaft, which turns the mill-stone. I think that the teeth of the two wheels were round sticks equally spaced round their felloes; this would be the best construction. The use of the word σκυτάλιον, "round stick", "handspake" for the teeth of a cog-wheel speaks for this supposition (53). So does also the figure in Heron's Pneumatics 2:32, where two gear-wheels work at right angles; here the teeth are shown as long sticks with parallel sides, not as the usual triangles. On the other hand, the bottom wheel of the hodometer, see p. 160 and fig. 62a, is shown with triangular teeth, though it is turned by a pin sitting on a hub at right angles to it. But here the construction is certainly effective.

In Saalburg (83, 105) has been found a lantern pinion, that is a small gear-wheel consisting of two parallel disks connected by a number of equally spaced round sticks. It is taken to be part of a horse-driven corn-mill. Probably it worked together with a wheel at right angles having sticks projecting not from the felloe but from the face, parallel to the axle, as they are found to-day in the irrigation wheels in the Mediterranean countries.

It would seem, then, that the use of the cog-wheel began with the rack-and-pinion arrangement of Ktesibios, and the endless screw of Archimedes, while the direct transmission is first known from the Antikythera instrument, which is from the 2. century B.C. The first mention of gear-wheels is from Vitruvius, about 25 B.C., in the water-mills, with the wheels at right angles. Next comes Heron, about 60 A.D., with the barulkos, which I refuse to take as a working engine. The gear-wheels then were developed by trial and error, big, wooden ones in the water-mills and, later, windmills; small, metal ones in clockwork. But it was not until 1675 that the correct solution was found, by Ole Rømer (73).

The rack-and-pinion was confined to toys and smaller instruments, and the worm-and-wheel gear, after a short flowering under Archimedes, was also reduced to toys and instruments, except for the re-setting apparatuses of the surgeons.

The lever

The lever is, as Heron has it, the oldest tool for increasing the power of man; see p. 52. It was used then as now as a simple tool for moving small burdens, levering stones into their places, and the like; a special form was the well-sweep, see p. 18. In large size it was used for oil- and wine-presses, as we find in Cato and Heron; here I may refer my reader to my book from 1932 (14).

The pulley

The single pulley has been known from very old times; it is shown in an Assyrian relief from about 870 B.C. (76). It is used for at bucket going down into a well. Also in ships it came into use very early.

The history of the triple pulley is more uncertain. Vitruvius calls it *trispastos*, see p. 143, which is Greek, but the *trispaston* which Oreibasios ascribes to Apellis or Archimedes is not a triple pulley, but a geared winch, as shown on p. 178. But it seems reasonable to assume that the Mechanical Problems in speaking of "two pulleys on two pieces of wood that come together against one another" describes a compound pulley, see p. 15. This would place it about 300 B.C.

Vitruvius calls a triple pulley *trispastos*, and a compound pulley of five sheaves *pentaspastos;* the word *polyspaston* he uses about a crane with three parallel sets of pulleys worked by three gangs of slaves; see p. 143, 147.

In Pappos, p. 1118, where he quotes Heron, see p. 55, the word πολύσπαστον, *polyspaston*, means a compound pulley, which in Arabic is called "the many for lifting", quite a good translation. This then has been Heron's word. Where Oreibasios, quoting Galenos (39), speaks of a polyspaston for a transportable re-setting spanner, it is not possible to tell if this is a compound pulley or a geared winch; Galenos says that it was invented by Archimedes. See p. 172.

The pulley was used, then as now, for hoisting and hauling; it went into the construction of the larger catapults.

The wedge

The wedge has been used from very old time for splitting wood and for cutting out marble slabs from quarries.

A very special use is seen in the perfume press mentioned by Heron and pictured in Pompeji (79). See p. 55 sq.

The screw

The lever is found everywhere in nature; the wedge is the direct descendant of the axe, if it is not the other way about. The roller and the wheel are also very old indeed, and the simple tackle-block was used, in principle anyway, the first time someone threw a rope over a bough or a stick to change a lift to a pull. But the use of the screw is the application of a mathematical construction to practical use.

According to Pappos, p. 1110, the screw line, "the snail on the cylinder", was first constructed by Apollonios of Perge, who lived about 265–170 B.C., a younger contemporary of Archimedes. It was used by

Archimedes for his water-snail, see p. 153 sqq., and for the endless screw, see p. 202.

Heron describes two uses of the screw for lifting burdens or for pulling a rope: the endless screw and the screw with a *tylos*, that is a peg engaging it from the side. The endless screw, as we have seen p. 202, was not used in larger engines for practical purposes except by surgeons. Oreibasios tells us that for the endless screw a lentil-shaped screw-thread was used, for moving a "tortoise" the screw-thread was square; see p. 171. Such tortoises are found in the engine of Andreas, who died in 217 B.C., and so was a contemporary of Archimedes. The screw went through a smooth hole in the tortoise, and a peg of iron or bronze was driven in from the side to engage the screw-thread; see p. 171. A single screw, κοχλίας ἁπλοῦς, moved one tortoise, a double screw, κοχλίας διπλοῦς, moved two tortoises, having screw-threads at both ends going round opposite ways. Here, as with the endless screw, the construction survived only in surgeons' engines, and was also here superseded by the female screw.

For presses the female screw was invented; first cut out in a block that was split and joined again; later made by the instrument described by Heron and probably invented by himself; see p. 135 sqq. And then the screw came into its own, as we see from a wall painting in Pompeji (81), showing a fullers' press with two screws, and from a magnificent specimen found in Herculanum with one screw only (34), and preserved in the museum there.

It was not possible to cut out a female screw in small holes in bronze or iron; so the smooth hole with the *tylos* was used by Heron in his water-level (52), in the screws for adjusting the sights; and it is found in surgical instruments, *specula matris*, of which several specimens are still extant (35, 136).

This is the history of the screw for moving and adjusting. The screw for holding down is quite another matter (82, 127). It was first invented, it seems, by goldsmiths for locking bracelets and the like, and it was made by a thread of metal being wound round outside a cylinder and inside a hole. For other purposes it did not come into use till it was possible to make male and female screws by means of a die and a screw-tap, but that was at a later time. Schramm has provided one of Biton's catapults with holding-down screws (6); but here κοχλίας does not mean a screw at all, but a drum round which a rope is wound.

Sundries

In Heron's Pneumatics we find mechanical implements outside the five powers. Most interest has been caused by his use of hot air or steam for producing a circular movement. There is an altar, where a fire is lit, and the hot air from the hollow altar streaming through four bent pipes makes puppets dance (63). Still more renowned is his steam turbine (64): a hollow ball is mounted on two brackets on the lid of a boiling vessel. One bracket is hollow and sends the steam into the ball, from which it escapes through two bent pipes that make the ball turn. You can hear people contend, on the strength of such play-things, that the ancient Greeks could have invented the steam engine, if only they did not have the slaves, which made such an invention superfluous. But slave labour was not cheap, and the presence of slaves did not prevent the invention of the watermill, which could be constructed by the means in hand. The construction of the steam engine had to wait until it was possible to make iron pipes and put them together with screws.

Another case in point is a small windmill described by Heron in his Pneumatics for working the pump of his water-organ (62). It disturbs the history of the windmill in Europe so much that R.J.Forbes (38) considers it a later addition to the manuscripts. This is hardly possible, since the same text and figure is found in Pseudo-Heron, whose date cannot be later than about 500 A.D. Since the Pneumatics exist only in a rather unfinished shape, it is quite possible that Heron did not live to complete it. I have suggested (29) that this windmill was invented by Heron, but that it never came beyond the stage of a suggestion on paper; unless it should be the origin of the eight-sailed turret-mill found in the Aegaean Islands, which is quite different from the four-sailed post-mill from the rest of Europe.

Inventors like Ktesibios and Heron strewed their inventions broadcast; but unless the invention found a fertile soil, it could not thrive. I should prefer not to seek for the cause of the failure of an invention in the social conditions till I was quite sure that it was not to be found in the technical possibilities of the time.

TANTUM

List of References

Page numbers at the beginning of each entry refer to the present volume.
Chapters from Aristoteles, Heron, Vitruvius, and Oreibasius, translated and interpreted, are listed on p. 224.

1. (p. 189) *Ammianus Marcellinus* 23:4:4–7.
2. (p. 10, 13) *Aristoteles:* Mechanical Problems. *In:* Aristotle: Minor Works. (The Loeb Classical Library.) London, Cambridge, Mass., 1936, p. 327–411. Greek and English.
3. (p. 10) *Athenaios:* The Deipnosophists. Book 11, p. 497 d–e.
4. (p. 10) The same: Book 4, p. 174 b–e.
   Athenaios the Mechanic. See: Rudolf Schneider: Griechische Poliorketiker III. Ref. 107.
5. (p. 11) *Bitons* Bau von Belagerungsmaschinen und Geschützen. Griechisch und deutsch von A. Rehm und E. Schramm. Abhandlungen der Bayerischen Akademie der Wissenschaften. Phil.-hist. Abteilung. N. F. Band 2, 1929.
6. (p. 205) The same: ch. 3.
7. (p. 191, 199) The same: ch. 4.
8. (p. 191) The same: ch. 5.
9. (p. 157) *British Museum.* Department of Greek and Roman Antiquities. A Guide to the Exhibition illustrating Greek and Roman Life. 2. ed. London 1920. Fig. 127, p. 120, and fig. 128, p. 121.
10. (p. 147, 199) *H. Bruun:* I monumenti degli Aterii. *In:* H. Brunn: Kleine Schriften, Band 1, Leipzig 1898, p. 84 sqq. and fig. 27.
11. (p. 199) *Cato:* De agricultura, ch. 18.
12. (p. 11) *Diels, Hermann:* Antike Technik. 2. Aufl. Leipzig und Berlin 1920, p. 23.
13. (p. 188) The same: p. 23, note 2.
    Diels, Hermann. See: Heron's Belopoiica. Ref. 49.
    See: Philon's Belopoiica. Ref. 91.
14. (p. 110, 203) *Drachmann, A. G.:* Ancient Oil Mills and Presses. Kgl. Danske Videnskabernes Selskab. Archæologisk-kunsthistoriske Meddelelser. Bind 1, Nr. 1. København 1932.
15. (p. 140) The same: p. 82, 84, 125 sqq.
16. (p. 199) The same: fig. 21, p. 151.
17. (p. 130) The same: fig. 25, p. 156.
18. (p. 76, 139) *Drachmann, A. G.:* Heron's screwcutter. Journal of Hellenic Studies, vol. 56, 1936, p. 72–77.
19. (p. 196) *Drachmann, A. G.:* Ktesibios, Philon and Heron. Acta historica scientiarum naturalium et medicinalium. Vol. 4, København 1948, p. 9.
20. (p. 202) The same: p. 16 sqq.
21. (p. 193) The same: p. 20–21, 26–31.
22. (p. 193) The same: p. 21–26.
23. (p. 19) The same: p. 77 sqq.
24. (p. 10) *Drachmann, A. G.:* On the alleged second Ktesibios. Centaurus, vol. 2, 1951, p. 1–10.

25. (p. 193) *Drachmann, A. G.:* The plane astrolabe and the anaphoric clock. Centaurus, vol. 3, 1954, p. 183–189.

26. (p. 11, 153) *Drachmann, A. G.:* The screw of Archimedes. Actes du VIIIᵉ Congrès international d'Histoire des Sciences Florence-Milan 1956. Vol. 3, Vinci (Firenze) et Paris, 1958, p. 940–943.

27. (p. 197) *Drachmann, A. G.:* Heron's dioptra and levelling-instrument. *In:* A History of Technology, vol. 3, Oxford 1937, p. 609–612.

28. (p. 11, 202) *Drachmann, A. G.:* How Archimedes expected to move the earth. Centaurus, vol. 5, 1958, p. 278–282.

29. (p. 206) *Drachmann, A. G.:* Heron's Windmill. Centaurus; vol. 7, 1961, p. 145–151.

30. (p. 190) *Drachmann, A. G.:* Caesar's *scorpio* and Philon's repeating catapult. Actes du IXᵉ Congrès International d'Histoire des Sciences, Barcelona-Madrid 1959. Barcelona, Paris, 1960, p. 203–205.

31. (p. 182) *Faust, Bernhardus:* De machinamentis ab antiquis medicis ad repositionem articulorum luxatorum adhibitis. Diss. Greifswald, 1912, p. 59.

32. (p. 182) The same: p. 60 and fig. XI.

33. (p. 201) *Feldhaus, F. M.:* Die Technik der Vorzeit, der geschichtlichen Zeit und der Naturvölker. Leipzig und Berlin 1914, *s. v.* Zahnrad.

34. (p. 205) *Feldhaus, F. M.:* Die Maschine im Leben der Völker. Basel, Stuttgart, 1964, Abb. 77, p. 121.

35. (p. 40, 205) The same: Abb. 78, p. 121.

36. (p. 151, 154) The same: Abb. 99, p. 138, and Abb. 100, p. 139.

37. (p. 147, 199) The same: Abb. 102, p. 143.

38. (p. 206) *Forbes, R. J.:* Power. *In:* A History of Technology, vol. 2, Oxford, 1957, p. 615.

39. (p. 204) *Galenos:* in Hippocatis De articulis commentariis, IV, 47 (Vol. XVIII, 1, p. 747, ed. Kühn).

40. (p. 194) *Georges, Karl Ernst:* Ausführliches Lateinish-Deutsches Handwörterbuch. 1–2. Leipzig 1879–1880. *s. v. choragium.*

41. (p. 144) The same: *s. v. rechamus.*

42. (p. 9) *B. Gille:* Machines. *In:* A History of Technology. Vol. 2. Oxford 1957, p. 629–658. (p. 633, 634 and 636.)
    Götze, Alfred. See: Moetefind, H. Ref. 82.

43. (p. 9) *Hall, A. R.:* Military Technology. *In:* A History of Technology. Vol. 2. Oxford 1957, p. 695–730. (p. 708, note 1.)
    Hauser, Fritz. See: Wiedemann, E. Ref. 137.

44. (p. 12) *Hero Alexandrinus.* Opera quae supersunt omnia. Vol. 1–5. Leipzig 1899–1914.

45. (p. 197) *Heron's* Automatic Theatre. Herons von Alexandria Druckwerke und Automatentheater … hrsg. von Wilhelm Schmidt. (Opera quae supersunt omnia, vol. 1) Leipzig 1899, p. 335–453.

46. (p. 197) The same: p. 395, note 1, and fig. 96a, p. 394.

47. (p. 197) The same: ch. 16. (p. 392–396).

48. (p. 199) The same: ch. 18 (p. 398–400).

49. (p. 186, 188) *Heron's* Belopoiica. Herons Belopoiika. Griechisch und deutsch

von H. Diels und E. Schramm. (Abhandlungen der kgl. preussischen Akademie der Wissenschaften. Jahrg. 1918. Phil.-hist. Kl. Nr. 2) Berlin 1918. Bild 19, p. 41.

50. (p. 24, 26, 163) *Heron's* Dioptra: MS. Codex Parisiacus inter supplementa Graeca no. 607. (The Mynas Codex). Description: Heronis Opera omnia 3, p. XII–XVI.

51. (p. 24, 159, 197) *Heron's Dioptra:* Text. Herons von Alexandria Vermessungslehre und Dioptra. Griechisch und deutsch von Hermann Schöne. (Opera quae supersunt omnia, vol. 3) Leipzig 1903, p. 187–315.

52. (p. 205) The same: ch. 4.

53. (p. 202) The same: ch. 34 (p. 294.)

54. (p. 20) *Heron's* Mechanics: MSS:
B. British Museum, Add. 23390.
L. University Library, Leiden, Cod. or. 51.

55. (p. 19) *Heron's* Mechanics: Text.
Carra de Vaux: Les mécaniques ou l'élévateur de Héron d'Alexandrie. Journal asiatique, 9. sér., vol. 1, p. 386–472; vol. 2, p. 152–269, 420–514. Paris 1893.
Herons von Alexandria Mechanik und Katoptrik. Hrsg. und übersetzt von L. Nix und W. Schmidt. (Opera quae supersunt omnia, vol. 2, fasc. 1) Leipzig 1900.

56. (p. 196) *Heron's* Pneumatics. Herons von Alexandria Druckwerke und Automatentheater, griechisch und deutsch hrsg. von Wilhelm Schmidt. (Opera quae supersunt omnia, vol. 1) Leipzig 1899.

57. (p. 155) The same: book 1, ch. 10, 11, 28.

58. (p. 156) The same: book 1, ch. 28.

59. (p. 13) The same: book 1, ch. 32; book 2, ch. 32.

60. (p. 196, 202) The same: book 1, ch. 34.

61. (p. 193) The same: book 1, ch. 42.

62. (p. 206) The same: book 1, ch. 43.

63. (p. 206) The same: book 2, ch. 3.

64. (p. 206) The same: book 2, ch. 11.

65. (p. 196) The same: book 2, ch. 32.

66. (p. 196, 202) The same: book 2, ch. 36.

67. (p. 154) *Hill, G. F. and H. W. Sandars:* Coins from the Neighbourhood of a Roman Mine in Southern Spain. Journal of Roman Studies, vol. 1, 1911, p. 100.

68. (p. 9) *A History of Technology.* Ed. by Charles Singer *et al.* Vol. 2, Oxford 1957. Vol. 3, Oxford 1957.

69. (p. 158) The same: Vol. 2, fig. 494, p. 546.

70. (p. 147, 199) The same: Vol. 2, fig. 603, p. 660.

71. (p. 184) *Hippokrates:* de articulis 72. (Oeuvres complètes d'Hippocrate ... par É. Littré. Tome 4, Paris, 1844, p. 40–44, 296 sq.)

72. (p. 30) *Hultsch, Fr.:* De Heronis mechanicorum reliquiis in Pappi collectione servatis. *In:* Commentationes philologae in honorem Theodori Mommseni ... Berlin 1877, p. 114–123. (p. 123, Note 14.)

73. (p. 200, 203) *Huygens, Chr.:* Oeuvres complètes, vol. 18. La Haye, 1934, p. 602 sq.

74. (p. 147, 199) *Jahn, O.* In: Berichte über die Verhandlungen der kgl. sächsischen Gesellschaft der Wissenschaften zu Leipzig. Phil.-hist. Kl. Bd. 13, 1861, p. 302, and Taf. IX, 2.

75. (p. 14) *Jan, K. von:* Die griechischen Saiteninstrumente. Programm Saargemünd, 1882. Cf. Baumeister, A.: Denkmäler des klassischen Altertums. 3. Band, München und Leipzig, 1889, *s. v.* Saiteninstrumente, p. 1541 sq.
    Krohn, F. See: Vitruvius Ref. 129.

76. (p. 203) *Laessøe, Jørgen:* Reflexions on modern and ancient oriental water works. Journal of Cuneiform Studies, vol. 7, 1953, fig. 1, p. 6.

77. (p. 9) *Lammert, Fr. In:* Pauly's Realencyclopädie *s. v.* Poliorketiker. (42. Halbband, 1952, col. 1385–1386.)

78. (p. 190) *Fr. Lammert. In:* Pauly's Realencyclopädie s. v. *Skorpion.* (2. Reihe, 5. Halbband, 1927, col. 585–586.)

79. (p. 56, 204) Mau, August: Pompeji in Leben und Kunst. 2. Aufl. Leipzig, 1908, Taf. IX, fig. 1, right; fig. 185, p. 352.

80. (p. 199) The same: fig. 187, p. 355.

81. (p. 205) The same: fig. 244, p. 414.

82. (p. 205) *Mötefindt, H.:* Zur Geschichte der Schraube. *In:* Studien zur vorgeschichtlichen Archäologie Alfred Götze zu seinem 60. Geburtstag dargebracht .. hrsg. von H. Mötefindt. Leipzig 1925, p. 199–206.
    Mommsen, Theodor. See: Hultsch, Fr. Ref. 72.

83. (p. 149, 203) *Moritz, L. A.:* Grain-Mills and Flour in Classical Antiquity. Oxford 1958, Plate 14, fig. c.

84. (p. 152) The same: p. 139.
    Mynas Codex. See Ref. 50.

85. (p. 12) *Neugebauer, O.:* Über eine Methode zur Distanzbestimmung Alexandria-Rom bei Heron. Kgl. Danske Videnskabernes Selskab. Historisk-filologiske Meddelelser, Bind 26, Nr. 2, 1938.

86. (p. 31) *Nix, L. In:* Heron's Mechanics p. XXII sqq.
    Nix, L. See: Heron's Mechanics. Ref. 55.

87. (p. 151, 154) Notizie degli Scavi di Antichità, vol. 3 (vol. 52) 1927, tav. IX.

88. (p. 12, 171) *Oreibasios.* Oribasii Collectionum medicarum reliqviae, Ed. Ioannes Raeder, Vol. 4, Lips. & Berol. 1933. (Corpus medicorum Graecorum edd. Academiae Berolinensis, Havniensis, Lipsiensis, 6:2:2.)

89. (p. 76, 79, 95) *Pappos:* MSS.
    P. Bibliothèque National, Paris. Codex grec 2368.
    V. Bibliotheca Apostolica Vaticana. Greco 218.

90. (p. 12) *Pappos:* Text.
    Pappi Alexandrini Collectionis quae supersunt ... edidit, latina interpretatione et commentariis instruxit Fridericus Hultsch, Vol. 3, part 1, Berlin 1878.

91. (p. 186, 188) *Philon's* Belopoiika ... Griechisch und Deutsch von H. Diels und E. Schramm. Abhandlungen der preussischen Akademie der Wissenschaften, Phil.-hist. Kl., Jahrgang 1918, Nr. 16. Berlin. 1919.

92. (p. 189) The same: ch. 34.

93. (p. 189) The same: ch. 43.

94. (p. 190) The same: ch. 51 sqq.

95. (p. 189) The same: ch. 60.

96. (p. 196) *Philon's* Pneumatics. Le livre des appareils pneumatiques et des machines hydrauliques, par Philon de Byzance édité ... par Carra de Vaux. Notices et

extraits des manuscrits de la bibliothèque nationale ... Vol. 38, 1903, Paris, p. 27–235.

97. (p. 196) The same: ch. 31.

98. (p. 156) The same: Appendix 1, ch. 2.

99. (p. 140) *Plinius:* Historia naturalis, book 18, ch. 317 (or 31 (74)).

100. (p. 201) *Price, Derek J. de Solla:* An Ancient Greek Computer. Scientific American, vol. 200, June 1959, p. 60–67.

101. (p. 159, 163) *Price, Derek J. de Solla:* On the Origin of Clockwork, Perpetual Motion Devices, and the Compass. Contributions from the Museum of History and Technology, Paper 6. (United States National Museum. Bulletin 218.) Washington, D.C., 1959, p. 84.

Ræder, Hans. See: Oreibasios Ref. 88.

Rehm, A. See: Biton Ref. 5.

102. (p. 154) *Rickard, T. A.:* Man and Metals. Vol. 1, New York and London, 1932, fig. 50, p. 425.

Rømer, Ole: See: Huygens, Chr. Ref. 73.

103. [vacant].

104. (p. 149) *Saalburg Jahrbuch,* Band 3, 1912 (1914), fig. 43, p. 89.

105. (p. 203) The same: Band 3, fig. 44, p. 90, and Taf. XVII.

Sandars, H. W. See: Hill, G. F. Ref. 67.

106. (p. 197) *Schmidt, W. In:* Herons Automatentheater, p. 395, Note 1, and Fig. 96a, p. 394.

Schmidt, Wilhelm. See: Heron's Automatic Theatre. Ref. 45.

                           Heron's Mechanics. Ref. 55.

                           Heron's Pneumatics. Ref. 56.

107. (p. 12, 186) *Schneider, Rudolf:* Griechische Poliorketiker. Mit den handschriftlichen Bildern herausgegeben und übersetzt.

I. Abhandlungen der kgl. Gesellschaft der Wissenschaften zu Göttingen. Phil.-hist. Klasse. N. F. Band 10, Nr. 1. Berlin 1908. (Apollodoros.)

II. Abhandlungen ... Band 11, Nr. 1. 1908 (1909). (Anonymus Byzantinus.)

III. Abhandlungen ... Band 12, Nr. 5. 1912. (Athenaios the Mechanic.)

108. (p. 191) The same: I: Taf. II, Fig. 6, 7; Taf. III, Fig. 8.

                               II: Taf. IV, Fig. 8; Taf. V, Fig. 9.

109. (p. 191) The same: I: Taf. XI, Fig. 40; Taf. XII, Fig. 41.

110. (p. 191) The same: III: Taf. I, Fig. 2.

111. (p. 191) The same: III: Taf. I, Fig. 3; Taf. VII, Fig. 2.

112. (p. 190) *Schneider, Rudolf. In:* Pauly's Realencyclopädie *s. v.* Geschütze. (13. Halbband, 1910, col. 1321.)

113. (p. 190) *Schneider, Rudolf:* Die antiken Geschütze der Saalburg. 3. Aufl. Berlin 1913, p. 31. (Quoted from Ref. 78.)

Schöne, Hermann, See: Heron's Dioptra. Ref. 51.

114. (p. 186) *Schramm, Erwin:* Die antiken Geschütze der Saalburg. Berlin 1918.

115. (p. 189) The same: p. 40–46, 75–78.

116. (p. 188) The same: p. 51–53, and Taf. 2.

117. (p. 189) The same: p. 57–59.

118. (p. 189) The same: p. 59–60.

119. (p. 190) The same: p. 60–62.
120. (p. 199) The same: p. 61.
121. (p. 189) The same: p. 62.
122. (p. 190) The same: p. 62, Note 1.
123. (p. 189) The same: p. 62–66.
124. (p. 189) The same: p. 70–74.
    Schramm, Erwin. See: Biton. Ref. 5.
                    Heron's Belopoiica. Ref. 49.
                    Philon's Belopoiica. Ref. 91.
125. (p. 33) *Selections* illustrating the history of Greek Mathematics, with an English Translation by Ivor Thomas. (Loeb Classical Library.) Vol. 1, London, Cambridge, Mass., 1951, p. 266 sqq.
126. (p. 10) *Susemihl, Fr.:* Geschichte der griechischen Litteratur der Alexandrinerzeit. Bd. 1, 1891, p. 734 sqq.
    Thomas, Ivor. See: Selections ... Ref. 125.
127. (p. 205) *Treue, Wilhelm:* Kulturgeschichte der Schraube ... München. 1955.
128. (p. 180) *Tzetzes:* Chiliades 2, v. 107–108 (hist. 35); 3, v. 61 (hist. 66).
    de Vaux, Carra: See: Heron's Mechanics. Ref. 55.
                    See: Philon's Pneumatics. Ref. 96.
129. (p. 11, 141) *Vitruvius:* De architectura libri decem. Edidit F. Krohn. Leipzig, 1912.
130. (p. 202) The same: Book 7, introductio ch. 14.
131. (p. 10, 156) The same: Book 9, ch. 8, 2 sqq.
132. (p. 10, 192) The same: Book 10, ch. 7, 5.
133. (p. 193) The same: Book 10, ch. 8, 3.
134. (p. 194, 196) The same: Book 10, ch. 8, 3-6.
135. (p. 188) The same: Book 10, ch. 10–12.
136. (p. 40, 205) *Vulpes, Benedetto. In:* Reale Museo Borbonico, Vol. 14, 1852, Tab. 36, fig. 1–2.
137. (p. 196) *Wiedemann, E. und Fritz Hauser:* Über die Uhren im Bereich der islamischen Kultur. Nova Acta Academiae caesar. Leopold.-Carol. germ. naturae curiosorum. Halle. Vol. 100, Nr. 5, 1915, p. 112 sqq.
138. (p. 11) *Wilamowitz-Moellendorff, Ulrich von:* Lesefrüchte. Hermes 65, 1930, p. 241–258. (p. 255.)

General Index

List of Greek Words

Arabic Words

List of Texts Translated